Heritage of the Petroleum Geologist

2003

Edited by

Robert C. Shoup

Deborah K. Sacrey

Charles A. Sternbach

Richard L. Nagy

Published by the Division of Professional Affairs
American Association of Petroleum Geologists
Tulsa, Oklahoma, U.S.A.
Printed in the U.S.A.

Cover Design: Rusty Johnson, AAPG
Production: AAPG
Printing: The Covington Group, Kansas City, Missouri

This and other AAPG publications are available from:

The AAPG Bookstore
P.O. Box 979
Tulsa, OK 74101-0979
U.S.A.
Telephone: 1-918-584-2555 or 1-800-364-AAPG (U.S.A., Canada)
Fax: 1-918-560-2652 or 1-800-898-2274 (U.S.A.)
www.aapg.org

Preface

Not so long ago, it was common for older geologists and geophysicists to sit together with younger employees for morning coffee or, on occasion, an afternoon beer. During those times, we would often hear tales of how this or that prospect got drilled or what happened to so-and-so while he (back then it was almost always a he) was sitting a rig.

For most companies, this getting together of old and new does not seem to happen much anymore, which is truly a shame. Those stories not only helped to build a level of camaraderie not seen much in the industry today, they also helped us to learn — to gain experience from those who had been there and done that.

So for those of you who miss those shared experiences or for those who have never had the opportunity to hear some of the old-timers' stories from the oil patch — here is your opportunity. Sit back, pour yourself a cup of coffee or a glass of beer, and enjoy!

The Southwestern Association of Petroleum Geologists met in Tulsa, Oklahoma, at Kendall College (later the University of Tulsa) on February 10, 1917, to form the American Association of Petroleum Geologists.

Guests swapped stories on the heritage of the petroleum geologists at the DPA/SIPES Convention Luncheon on March 12, 2002, during the AAPG Annual Meeting in Houston, Texas.

Introduction

By Robert C. Shoup

In the early planning stages of the 2002 AAPG Annual Meeting, to be held in Houston, convention chairman Jeff Lund and vice chairs Charles Sternbach and Deborah Sacrey decided on the convention theme of "Our Heritage, Key to the Future." In planning the Division of Professional Affairs luncheon for that meeting, I felt strongly about keeping that theme and honoring our heritage. It was decided that not only would we get Michel T. Halbouty to be our luncheon speaker, but we would invite industry notables to be our guests at the luncheon, each "hosting" a table. Because there is no such thing as a "free lunch," we also asked each of the guests to provide answers to the following questions:

- What was your proudest accomplishment?

- What was your biggest disappointment?

- What advice would you give us?

The answers were compiled in a booklet that was handed out to all attendees of the DPA luncheon. The booklet was an immediate success, and we have received numerous requests for copies.

In light of that success, AAPG's Division of Professional Affairs has agreed to subsidize the cost of this book. Each of the luncheon's heritage guests was contacted, along with other individuals who had been unable to attend the luncheon. We asked all of them to provide one more item — an anecdotal story that

would fit with their proudest accomplishment, their biggest disappointment, or their advice.

What follows are the recollections, stories, and advice of 43 of the most successful people in the industry.

What is it that separates successful individuals from the crowd? What is it that they do or have that allows them to be successful — or are they just lucky? Luck certainly plays a role, particularly in the oil and gas business, yet the ingredients to success are certainly more than that. Psychologists and business consultants have looked for years for the answers to these questions, generally concluding that there are too many variables to success to define one or two key ingredients.

Perhaps that is so. I am certainly not a psychologist, and I do not have an M.B.A. However, in reading the stories and the advice of these 43 people, I certainly sense a pattern — a key to the success of these individuals. They all believed deeply in what they were doing, and they had the perseverance to do what it took to see their ideas through.

As you read the stories in this book, I expect that you will at times find them to be thought provoking and at times amusing. It is my hope that you will also find this book to be inspirational.

The stories included herein are part of the vast heritage that we as petroleum geoscientists have. Where would we be without our heritage? Every concept, every idea would need to be regenerated, with the result that the world would have certainly run out of oil and gas — not because we would have exhausted the supply. Rather, we could not have sustained a pace of drilling that would have matched the demand.

The ideas behind every well that we drill today have been built on the ideas of others who have walked before us. Our heritage is a rich one and includes many noted individuals — Lyell, Hutton, Drake, Joiner, Platt, Leverson, and Halbouty — as well as other people who have contributed to this publication, to name but a few. But just as important, our heritage also includes those individuals that few may have heard of — those who took the time and effort to take you under their wing and serve as your mentors.

I remember being on a field trip many years ago. We had stopped at an outcrop noted for containing fossil sharks' teeth. None of the trip participants had any trouble finding a good collection of teeth, whereas I found none. As we were nearing the time when we needed to leave, my good friend and mentor Blair Parrott came up and asked what was wrong. I confessed that I was not finding any sharks' teeth. He bent down and pointed to a slightly darker spot in the shale, noting that this is what they look like in the outcrop. Almost as if by magic, I saw dozens of sharks' teeth where minutes before I had seen none. I too was able to get a nice collection of sharks' teeth.

This story illustrates to me the best of mentoring.

Blair, as a good mentor, observed that I was having difficulty and approached me. Just as important, I had to be willing to admit that I was struggling — something our pride, or fear of ridicule, often prevents. Most important, I realized that you can't find something until you know what it looks like.

For those of you who are students or are just beginning your career, look for people who are willing to be your mentors — people who will show you the ropes. Go to them and ask them to be your mentors. You will find that most of them will be honored that you asked, and will be more than willing to provide guidance.

For those of you who are well established in your career, you should seek both to be a mentor and to have a mentor. You are at the point where you can serve as a mentor to students and to those just beginning their careers. You are likely to find the experience both rewarding and rejuvenating. At the same time, you should get to know consultants and independents so that you can, if you desire or need to, make that transition in your career.

This book is therefore dedicated to all those individuals, noted and anonymous, who have been or will be mentors.

Table of Contents

The Past Is a Beacon for the Future

Michel T. Halbouty

Note: The article below was Michel T. Halbouty's address at the DPA/SIPES luncheon at the Annual Meeting of AAPG in Houston, Texas, on March 12, 2002.

I am pleased to have the opportunity to speak to this group today. I will try to portray to you some of the meaning of our profession and some of its effect on society.

The theme of AAPG's 2002 meeting is "Our Heritage: Key to Global Discovery," and it is most appropriate and timely that this topic is selected and presented at the beginning of this century. It is a subject that will have a profound effect on our profession in the future. We — as petroleum geologists — have built an incomparable heritage of knowledge that is readily available for our endeavors of the future.

When I became a member of our profession 72 years ago, I picked up the petroleum-geology heritage that was available. There wasn't much. Petroleum geology was still in its infancy, and those of us who were in the profession had to crawl and strive for any type of information or available data. Our correlating mediums were micropaleontology and drillers' logs. Because of the scarcity of information, we worked hard, and made our findings available to each other. Therefore, those who later entered the profession were able to step into petroleum geology with the knowledge accumulated up to the time of their entrance into the profession.

Gee — I look back at what I knew at the time I entered the profession to what I know now, and it seems I have gone through countless hours and days of just keeping up with the advances. There was very little heritage to lean on, but what was available was absorbed with relish.

Now, the science of geology, in which our petroleum geology is just a segment, is the most intriguing of all sciences. The story of this earth, the evolution and destruction of continents, the processions of life which since the beginning of time have passed over its surface are the basics of the science of geology.

It really became a science during the Middle Ages, when the philosophers of nature undoubtedly were influenced by the Aristotelian elements of "fire, air, earth and water." They sedulously examined the objects of nature in their natural state and traversed the fields, the mountains, the woods and the waters, and checked the oceans and the shores. By these efforts, they became proficient in natural knowledge — thus they established the beginning of the heritage of geology.

Geology has grown and advanced on the balance scale of probability rather than the rigid, less flexible framework of mathematics; thus geology always has been an *inexact*, speculative science.

Commonly suffering from speculation beyond the limits of observation and experience, geologic hypotheses and theories have been promulgated and dissipated, but not without some benefit to each succeeding generation of earth scientists. It is precisely this inexactness of our science which makes it such a great challenge to practice it.

I firmly believe that there is no factor vital to the human race which the science of geology does not explore or participate in to some extent, however remote. From time to time, I reflect on conditions that exist in the world, and I conclude — over and over again — that the world's people could not meet their many human needs without geologists, who discover the supply of natural resources vital to their welfare and comfort.

Geologists and geophysicists together are imperative to the future petroleum-energy stability of this nation and the world. We are needed to find the oil and gas that remain to be found, both onshore and offshore. Without us, no oil and gas would be discovered. In this regard, our profession cannot survive without exploration, and neither can the basic energy security of this nation. We are tied together; if one falters, so does the other. This is why I refer to our profession as the indispensable segment of the science of geology. We are fortunate to be involved in this extraordinary effort.

Our profession of petroleum geology indeed had a unique beginning. Petroleum geology's first item of legacy began in 1842, when Sir William Logan, the Montreal geologist who was director of the Geological Survey of Canada, studied the petroleum springs at Gaspé, in his native province of Quebec, and stated that they were located and associated with anticlinal folding. Logan's comments on these seeps were the first expression of the anticlinal theory with relation to oil accumulation.

Many geologists of that time could not agree with the theory, and it became one of the most controversial of subjects, particularly on both sides of the Atlantic Ocean. For about 40 years, the controversy continued between geologists. In 1880, one of the more accomplished geoscientists of the times, J. P. Lesley, referred to the theory as a "deservedly forgotten superstition." This was 21 years after Drake had discovered oil at Titusville, Pennsylvania, in 1859. Still, the top geologists of the world argued about a concept that Sir Logan had proposed in 1842.

In 1883, John Galey, the wildcatter, and William A. Erseman, a Pennsylvania oil operator, independently informed their friend, Dr. Israel C. White, a professor of geology at West Virginia University, that their land and drilling observations indicated there definitely was some relation between existing oil and gas fields and anticlines.

White immediately became interested. He diligently studied the concept. He went into the field, studied the rocks, and finally concluded that the theory was sound. He believed in it so strongly that he took leave of his position at West Virginia University to form a company and drill a well, using the anticlinal theory as its basis. The result was the discovery of the first significant production in West Virginia. White then returned to the university a much wiser, wealthier, and more respected professor of geology.

Later, White announced his rediscovery of the anticlinal theory, but in doing so he acknowledged freely the priority of others. This he made clear in his 1885 paper, "Geology of Natural Gas." That paper was followed by the publication, in April 1892, of another on the anticlinal theory, in the *Bulletin* of the Geological Society of America.

Undoubtedly, these two papers by White gave petroleum geology its first status and the permanency of the anticlinal theory. Thus, Dr. Israel C. White is credited by historians as the founder of our petroleum-geology profession. Incidentally, White was the third president of AAPG.

Now — the most important segment of this story is the fact that as celebrated geoscientists were arguing among themselves as to the validity of a concept, wildcatters who were not formally trained in the science of geology extolled the virtues of the concept, which turned out to be accurate.

Even after Dr. White's intervention, petroleum geology had numerous difficulties remaining a respected profession. Many errors and misconceptions by geologists — and condemnations by geologists of areas which turned out to be productive by random wildcatters — caused the managers in the oil industry to be not only reluctant but also most hesitant to openly recognize the profession.

Although the early practitioners of our branch of geology were beset by great problems, they were true investigators and, in a scientific manner, tried to form concepts on a subject which was new to them. They stuck their necks out, and some were "chopped off." However, through the efforts of these stubborn scientific pioneers, the fundamental pieces of petroleum geology gradually were put into proper place. The fact that these early petroleum geologists were at times wrong did not discourage their search for the truth. For the past 110 years, their discoveries, mistakes, confusions, and solutions have given us the total results of their efforts — a remarkable heritage.

The heritage of geologic fundamentals that was handed down to us was accompanied by another kind of inheritance — the application of common sense, courage, stubbornness, and intestinal fortitude in the search for oil — from the nonprofessionals, the wildcatters. They drilled thousands of wells, leaving us volumes of critical geologic information. These daring wildcatters gave petroleum geology new concepts, new ideas, and different viewpoints. They gave greater strength to a profession which they generally regarded as inadequate and inefficient.

Their accomplishments and input to our profession further prove that scientists are occasionally helped by the bold, imaginative, creative thinking and exploration of those who are not formally educated or even trained in a scientific discipline.

Now, let's talk about the "suppressor" — the know-it-all! There are some in our profession who are prone to suppress unusual ideas of their coworkers, putting them down for even thinking differently than they. It is the know-it-all who stifles brilliant ideas with the overbearing arrogance born of ignorance, because it is from these unyielding, onerous, omnipotent thinkers that we learn that all is not as it seems and that often brilliant minds are forced to veer from the truth.

Those "suppressors" generate apprehension and fear that prevent free and creative thought. There is no question that fear stifles boldness in the explorationist — not being willing to express an unusual exploration idea or concept for fear of losing a job or being shuttled into an inferior position. As a result, creativity and boldness in the exploratory effort are discouraged by rebuke and fear, which prevent new exploratory thinking. Instead, mediocrity, "going along with the boys," and "implied assent by silence" are, unfortunately, the credos of many people who are engaged in petroleum exploration.

As hunters for petroleum, we should not ever be afraid to experiment with an unusual idea or concept — and once you believe that you are correct in your analyses, stick with it and go for it. It may be a failure, but at least you gave your conviction a chance. I remember the often-quoted phrase, "The greatest risk is not taking one!"

As part of this presentation, I will go back many decades and relate to you three incidents I remember vividly that portray the optimism, pessimism, and emotions of explorationists — and wildcatters.

First incident — Optimism

I happened to be in the same elevator with Roy Cullen, who was one of the pillars of Houston and, at the time, one of the most successful independents in the petroleum business. I am referring to the year 1935 — 67 years ago.

He looked at me and said, "Aren't you the geologist associated with Glenn McCarthy?"

I said, "Yes, sir!"

He invited me to get off the elevator on his floor, because he wanted to show me something. He took me to a large cabinet where many gadgets were displayed.

He said, "I don't believe in geology — it hasn't found me anything, but you see this one," pointing to one of the items in the case, "I found the O'Conner Field with that," and he pointed to one after the other, naming the fields the gadget had found.

I stood in awe of what Mr. Cullen was telling and showing me. As far as he was concerned, he had absolute proof that those gadgets had found him the tremendous wealth he made from oil. His belief in those ingenious articles was unquestionable and un-assailable.

Although neither of us believed in the other's method in searching for petroleum, we became good friends — a youngster in his twenties and a wildcatter in his seventies.

I learned something very important from that episode — *that the power of conviction is absolute in whichever direction it is subjected!*

Next incident — Pessimism

I was attending an American Petroleum Institute meeting in Chicago and ran into a friend who was an independent I had not seen in a couple of years. We visited over a drink, and a bellman to whom I had previously indicated I was expecting a call advised me that the call was ready. As I got up to leave, I told my friend I hoped this would be good news of a wildcat I was drilling.

When I came back, my friend asked if I had good news, and I told him, "No, it's a dry hole."

He said, "Does that surprise you?"

I replied that it certainly did, because I had expected a discovery.

He said he expected every wildcat he ever had anything to do with to be a dry hole. *I was startled.*

I said, "That's total pessimism!"

I also told him I expected my every wildcat to produce, and if any were dry holes, I just looked around the corner for the next wildcat.

He didn't stay in wildcatting very long. Pessimism is not for the hunter of oil and gas.

As I have stated over the years, I firmly believe that positive thoughts generate positive results, and pessimistic thoughts generate negative results.

Last incident — Emotions

I have always said that wildcatting brings euphoria and heartaches — but some heartaches linger!

I've drilled thousands of wells, but the greatest anguish of all was my first well in Alaska. I studied Alaska's geology — I made several trips, studying the rocks on foot with a rifle and a pack on my back. I traveled by truck and bush planes, and I was convinced that oil would be found in that cold and fore-boding area known as a territory of the United States.

All of my fieldwork was done in the late 1940s and early 1950s — more than 50 years ago — and to my knowledge, no one, large or small, was even thinking of exploring in Alaska. I leased thousands of acres from the territory, and I was stuck with the provision that if it became a state, all my leases would be null and void except those on which actual production of oil or gas existed.

Here I was — the first independent to go into and explore in Alaska. I might say that it took not only intestinal fortitude but, to put it in the proper vernacular, unmitigated guts! I was a small but very adventuresome independent, and Alaska attracted me like a moth to light.

I moved a brand-new rig from Bakersfield to Long Beach, California, to Seward, Alaska, and spudded my first well 16 days after I signed the rig contract. Even though I had geologists and petroleum engineers in my company who could have been involved with moving the rig and drilling the well, I was so captivated with the possibilities of a discovery in that remote area that I chose to supervise and have *fun* doing it all myself.

Twelve wildcats were drilled with the rig — I found one small gas field.

After 15 years, Alaska overwhelmed me, and I got out. I had met bitter disappointment after disappointment in a giant area that I had extolled — an area where I had marched in alone to lease and drill my most significant career wildcat.

In later years, I was visiting with several young geologists at an AAPG Annual Meeting and one said to me, "Mr. H., I understand you lost many millions in Alaska."

I said, "Yes, that's true — but I still consider my Alaskan venture a success."

He asked, "How can you possibly consider it a success, losing that much money?"

I hesitated, looked him in the eye, and said, "It was a success to me, because I had the desire to do it — *and I did it.*"

So the question arises, "Why did I do it?"

I did it because it was the greatest challenge I had ever faced, and I confronted the challenge head-on. I challenged the challenge! I was prepared to accept the outcome, whatever it was, but more important, as a wildcatter, *I had a firm belief, a strong conviction,* that I would discover oil — lots of it — in Alaska, and I set out to prove my conviction.

Success is measured in many ways other than by money. The Alaska venture was a tremendous display of effort for someone as small as I was — of meeting obstacles and challenges in a very hostile environment, with virtually no support or ready availability of materials.

The venture in Alaska is my proudest effort — and yet, after all these years, my first Alaskan wildcat remains the most bitter disappointment of my career. That well was a *killer.* When I was on the derrick floor at about midnight in bitter cold — 25 below zero — and the last objective was cored and found dry, it affected every fiber of my body and left me limp and full of depressive emotions. *I was totally crushed.* I had put so much of myself in that one well that the unexpected dry hole devastated me. The disappointment was so severe, I literally cried.

I remember many of my wildcats — some of the good ones and some of the bad ones — but that Alaskan wildcat I drilled 45 years ago gnaws at me to this very day. It proves that in the throes of success, there are unexpected and sometimes bitter disappointments that are beyond comprehension or acceptance.

In three months — God willing — I will be 93 years old. I am definitely in my twilight's twilight zone. Whatever I have done or didn't do, whatever were my successes or failures, above all, I was always exceedingly proud to be a geoscientist — a student and disciple of the earth. I would be well rewarded if any of my efforts contribute to the heritage which is ours to pass to those who follow us.

I have enjoyed visiting with you today — and I extend my heartiest wish for all of you to enjoy good searching for the oil and gas which the world will be needing for the future.

Thank you for listening.

Heritage of the Petroleum Geologist

Michel T. Halbouty
Houston, Texas

Note: The article below was Michel T. Halbouty's presidential address at the Annual Convention of AAPG in Los Angeles, California, on April 11, 1967. It was printed originally in the AAPG *Bulletin*, v. 51, no. 7 (July 1967), p. 1179–1184.

The heritage left us by the early petroleum geologists has been ignored and practically forgotten. Those geologists should be remembered not only for their achievements, but also for having been well-rounded, true geologists who applied all facets of our science to their endeavors. Their methods and contributions should be "dusted off" and restudied, and once again used as guideposts for our future thinking. The intrepidity, firm persuasion, and complete dependence of these men on sheer intellect created the basic concepts which resulted in world-wide, successful petroleum exploration. In order to meet our exploration requirements of the future, the profession must develop more original ideas, and not be afraid to push those ideas forward into fruition. We must once again become true geologists — well-rounded and knowledgeable. It is only then that we can emulate successfully our predecessors, who as scientists and free-thinkers conquered their problems through their strong courage of conviction; it is only then that we shall have paid our debt to them for the inheritance which they left us and our debt to our profession — for the heritage that we build upon and leave for our successors.

On February 10, 1917, this Association was founded; thus we are 2 months and 1 day into our second 50 years. I believe we have good reason to be proud of our first half century since 1917 — the year our country entered the First World War — 50 years and 5 days ago.

There were also important events in the petroleum industry that year — 1917. They include the founding of Phillips Petroleum, the formation of Humble Oil and Refining Company, Shell's discovery of the Bolivar Coastal fields in Venezuela, the first gravity survey of a salt dome — in Germany — the discussion by two young physicists named William Peter Haseman and John Clarence Karcher of the use of seismic waves to determine subsurface structures, and the confiscation of all private oil properties in Russia.

Also, in 1917 an official of the Bureau of Mines looked over the U. S. oil supply situation and said that the United States faced "... a national crisis of the first magnitude." He predicted nothing ahead except declining production, rising prices, and an acute oil shortage. Until then the United States had produced approximately 4 billion barrels of oil in 58 years.

Well, what happened? Since then we have produced 75 billion barrels of oil and have 39 billion barrels more in reserves, to say nothing of vast reserves of natural gas.

Those were the days, too, when young men were being advised by the elders of our industry to get into some other field of endeavor because the oil industry was "all washed up."

I believe the major share of credit for the reversal of that pessimistic trend of thinking was due to the men who met 50 years ago and organized our Association. This is an important part of our heritage. Webster defines heritage as "... that which is inherited, inheritance; hence, the lot, condition, or state into which one is born; a birthright."

From the beginning, geology has grown and advanced on the balance-scale of probability rather than in the rigid, less flexible framework of mathematics; thus geology always has been an inexact, speculative science. Commonly suffering from speculation beyond the limits of observation and experience, geological hypotheses and theories have been promulgated and dissipated, but not without some benefit to each succeeding generation of earth scientists. It is precisely this inexactness of our science which makes it such a great challenge. It takes real courage to meet this challenge.

Thus, the philosophers of nature during the Middle Ages undoubtedly were influenced by the "Aristotelian elements" of fire, air, earth, and water. Werner and the Neptunists, and Hutton and the Plutonists, gained many of their ideas from the published works of Agricola on mineralogy. Each of these men had a heritage on which he progressed in his own pursuits. These men, their forebears, their colleagues, and their successors all contributed in some measure to our heritage.

Lesser known, yet very influential men, such as John Walker, a professor and a naturalist, established the existing foundation for seeking and probing into the earth. Walker's influence must have been most profound because among his students are the names of James Hutton, John Playfair, James Hall, and Robert Jameson — all of whom later became great geologists and scientists. In 1779, just 188 years ago, at the University of Edinburgh during one of a series of lectures on geology, John Walker told his students:

"The objects of nature themselves must be sedulously examined in their native state, the fields and the mountains must be traversed, the woods and the waters must be explored, the ocean must be fathomed, and the shore scrutinized by everyone that would become proficient in natural knowledge."

As geologists, by inclination and thorough training, we should be imbued with a love for exploration of the earth in order to solve its many mysteries. To be recipients of the geological heritage handed down to us, we can do no better than follow the advice of Walker.

The heritage of the petroleum geologist, that avocational specialty which most of us assembled here have adopted as our professional domain, has a broad base, developed and matured by scientists and non-scientists alike. It is built on the labors and achievements of our predecessors, who, by meticulous observation of nature and careful deduction therefrom, laid the scientific foundation of the profession. It is also built, in no small measure, by the successes, failures, and experiences of many non-professionals — such as the non-scientists who probed beneath the surface of the earth in search of hydrocarbons.

Among our early petroleum-minded predecessors who contributed to our heritage, there comes to my mind Sir William Elwood Logan, the Montreal geologist who was director of the Geological Survey of Canada for more than a quarter of a century. In 1842, or 17 years before the birth of the oil industry, Sir William Logan studied the petroleum springs at Gaspé in his native Province of Quebec, and stated that they were located and associated with anticlinal folding. As far as I know, Logan's comments on these seeps were the first expression of the anticlinal theory with relation to oil accumulation.

Another of these early pioneers was Henry D. Rogers, once head of the Pennsylvania Geological Survey, who gave a remarkable lecture at the University of Glasgow in 1860, shortly after the Drake well came in, on the subject of the distribution and probable origin of petroleum in western Pennsylvania.

It was at this time that discussions of the anticlinal theory as it relates to petroleum became one of the most controversial of geological subjects. The participants include the versatile but sometimes erratic T. Sterry Hunt, Ebenezer Andrews, J. P. Lesley, and the brothers, William and Henry D. Rogers.

This select group might be called the instigators of interest in petroleum geology, although they did equally well in confusing the subject, with the result that it took another 20 years before Dr. Israel C. White actually founded the petroleum geology profession.

Lesley, for example, after his early pronouncement

of the anticlinal theory in 1860, changed his mind and vigorously denounced the theory in a paper published in 1863. As recently as 1880 he referred to the theory as that "... now deservedly forgotten superstition." He was indirectly replying to the Austrian geologist, Hans Hofer, who was taking a new and serious affirmative interest in the theory.

Three years later, independently, John Galey, the wildcatter, and William A. Erseman, a Pennsylvanian oil operator, called White's attention to their field and drilling observations that there definitely was some relation between existing gas fields and anticlines. White immediately became interested. He diligently studied the concept — he went into the field, studied the rocks, and finally concluded that the theory was sound. He believed in it so strongly that he decided to take leave of his position as professor of geology at West Virginia University to form a company which drilled a well, using the anticlinal theory as its basis.

The result was the discovery and establishment of the first significant production in West Virginia. White then returned to the university a much wiser, a wealthier, and a more respected professor of geology.

Later White announced his re-discovery of the anticlinal theory but in doing so he acknowledged freely the priority of others. This he made clear in his 1885 paper on "Geology of Natural Gas." That paper was followed by the publication in April, 1892, of another on the anticlinal theory in the *Bulletin* of The Geological Society of America. There is no doubt that these two papers by White gave petroleum geology its first status, and the anticlinal theory permanency. Incidentally, White was the third president of our Association.

Petroleum geology had numerous problems facing it in order to remain a respected profession. Many errors and misconceptions by geologists, and condemnations by geologists of areas which turned out to be productive, caused the oil industry to be not only reluctant but also most hesitant to recognize the profession.

Although the founders of our branch of geology were beset by great difficulties, they were true investigators and in a scientific manner tried to form concepts on a subject which was new to them. They "stuck their necks out," and some were "chopped off." However, through the efforts of these stubborn pioneers, the pieces fundamental to petroleum geology gradually were put into proper place. The fact that these early petroleum geologists were, at times, wrong did not discourage their endeavors to arrive at the truth.

Through their discoveries, their mistakes, their confusions, and their solutions, we have had given to us the total results of their efforts; *this* is our heritage. It consists of geologic truths, and carries no obligation — except that we carry on from where our predecessors left off. Thus, this heritage must be a continuum, based on more study, exploration, curiosity, failure, success, and total effort so that we, in turn, may hand down to our geological successors a heritage greater than that which we received. We must not break the continuum. This is our responsibility to geologists of the future and to the science of geology, and of petroleum geology in particular.

The heritage of geological fundamentals that was handed down to us was accompanied by another kind of inheritance — the application of common sense, courage, stubbornness, and intestinal fortitude in the search for oil — from the non-professional — the wildcatter!

Such men include Edwin L. Drake, the railroad conductor, and his associates who explored, experimented, and gave birth to the petroleum industry in 1859. Another is John Galey, an adventurer in the oil fields, who was bold enough to suggest and promote in 1883 a practical application of the anticlinal theory when the geologists chose to criticize and write papers about it.

Still another is a woodsman named Pattillo Higgins who learned to know and love what he called the "signs of nature," and thereby led Captain Anthony Lucas, a marine engineer, to the discovery in 1901, in the dawn of a new century, of the gusher at Spindletop that brought forth the liquid fuel age.

To these I would add the name of Marrs McLean, a man, educated as a lawyer, who made a living selling advertising, and then promoted oil leases but who conceived the idea in 1923 that oil could be found on the flanks of salt domes. His concept was rejected by the most renowned petroleum geologists of his day. Nevertheless, McLean's theory became completely accepted by our profession in 1926 when my first employer, Miles Frank Yount, bought the idea and leases from McLean and was rewarded with a new great discovery at Spindletop — the opening of the vast reserves on the flanks of this historic salt dome.

I could not resist mention of another adventurer who had an idea based on an unsound theory by a self-styled geologist, an idea which brought forth the greatest oil discovery in the history of the North American continent, in Rusk County, Texas, in 1930. His name was Columbus Marion Joiner. He was a 70-year-old promoter whom everyone called "Dad." He accepted the word of Dr. A. D. Lloyd — a man who was trained as a veterinarian but who delved into geology as a hobby — that oil was to be found in East Texas. Almost every geologist — and I might add geophysicist — of that period had come to regard the area as worthless and condemned it as an economic graveyard that would be studded with dry holes. In fact, by the time Joiner and Lloyd arrived on the scene nothing but dry holes dotted the sandhills of East Texas.

Nevertheless, Lloyd wrote Joiner a letter telling him almost exactly the depth at which he would strike oil. He also told him why. We know now that scientifically his reasoning was wrong, but we also know now that what Lloyd and Joiner combined to accomplish led our profession to a greater recognition of the vast potential of the stratigraphic trap.

The books are full of examples of men finding oil by the "seat of their pants" in areas where geologists feared to tread. The reason for this fear is that geologists had forgotten — or never learned — the words of John Walker. They failed to examine on the ground "the objects of nature"; they failed to traverse "the fields and the mountains"; they did not explore "the woods and the waters"; above all, they failed to examine the rocks.

These daring wildcatters gave petroleum geology new concepts, new ideas, and different viewpoints; they gave greater strength to the profession which they generally regarded as inadequate and inefficient. Their accomplishments further prove that scientists are helped sometimes by the bold, imaginative, creative thinking and exploration of those who are not formally educated, or even trained in the scientific method.

Of course, it is a compliment to our profession that these suddenly discovered ideas were seized on by our predecessors, placed in the proper frame of nature's jig-saw puzzle, and put to use to find many times more hydrocarbons.

Scientists whom many of us have known or know now — E. T. Dumble, J. A. Taff, Charles N. Gould, Charles Eckes, W. A. J. M. van der Gracht, W. E. Wrather, E. DeGolyer, Alexander Deussen, Paul Weaver, Ben Belt, A. I. Levorsen, Wallace Pratt, Frederic Lahee, Frank Morgan, Lewis G. Weeks, Frank Clark, Sam Grinsfelder, and Ira Cram, and a host of others, most of them members of our own Association since its founding a half century ago — have added to the heritage handed them and have brought us to the point where we now are.

To this list one might add a host of better and lesser known men of geology who have contributed their ideas and concepts, large and small, important and less consequential, to the reservoir of knowledge we now have available in the field of earth science as it applies to petroleum. We might also add the names of numerous non-scientists, in addition to Drake, Galey, Higgins, Lucas, McLean, Yount, and Joiner, whose natural instincts or good fortune have led them to geological achievements which have benefited all of us and all of mankind.

Each of us also might recall some men who have stifled brilliant ideas with the overbearing arrogance born of ignorance, because it is from men such as these that we learn that all is not as it seems in this inexact science, and that without open minds we commonly veer from the truth.

Thus this heritage of the petroleum geologist is based on the works of many men, those who have been right and those who, from time to time, have been dramatically wrong.

This heritage serves as the framework and guidepost to our knowledge of petroleum geology. We must build on it and hand down to the next generation a stronger and broader heritage of knowledge. We must boldly and creatively seek new knowledge, through ingenuity, and, although beset with failures and wrong turns, we must ferret out this new knowledge and add it to our heritage.

What about our shortcomings as petroleum geologists? The truth is that, as a whole, we have failed many times to employ our science properly. We have depended too much on other disciplines to guide us and have not practiced our science as it should be practiced — in fact, *we have lost, in some measure, direct contact with the earth.* By losing this contact, we have lost our curiosity for its mysteries and, in turn, we are becoming less creative and less courageous.

We have subjected ourselves to routine thinking, without probing and seeking to understand better the true meaning of our science. We have become afraid to experiment mentally into an unusual concept or idea. Ironically, those who employ or use our knowledge do not expect our bold and creative ideas always to be right. A major-company official said to me not long ago, "Show me a geologist or geophysicists who is afraid to make a recommendation for fear of his making an error in judgment, and I will show you a man who is not only stealing my company's money and time but one who is hardly worth being called a scientist."

What this executive was saying is that such fear stifles boldness in the explorationist. In short, this executive was complaining that some geologists and geophysicists are not willing to take a chance — and are not willing to express an unusual exploration idea or concept for fear of losing their jobs. As a result, creativity and boldness in the exploratory effort are discouraged by this fear of failure, and nothing is contributed to exploratory thinking; instead, mediocrity, "going along with the boys," and implied assent by silence are the credos of many who are engaged in petroleum exploration.

What John Walker said in 1779 is as applicable

today as ever. The true explorationist *must* get out of the office, go into the field, the plains, and valleys, traverse the woods, and the mountains, and the seashores; he *must* look hard at the rocks, and at any other "signs of nature" that he can find.

Pattillo Higgins observed the "signs of nature," and led all men to a new age of progress — yet he was not a geologist. He went to the top of a little rise in a flat prairie and observed that there was a sandy loam where clay was supposed to exist, a peculiar substance in the soil which had a "waxy" feel and which later was named "paraffin dirt" by geologists; and he also tasted brackish water in wells of fresh water. These "signs of nature" enabled him to proclaim openly that he could drill wells on that spot which would produce tens of thousands of barrels of oil daily. He was denied by experts, including geologists, and even scorned by his neighbors. But his faith in what he believed led to one of the world's most important mineral discoveries of all time.

Ben Belt, the scientist, climbed in an old automobile and crossed and criss-crossed the arid land of west Texas, facing hired gunmen guarding "posted" signs or ranchers with shotguns, to seek out rocks that would tell him what he wanted to know. When he had finished his study of the rocks, and plotted his data on his maps, he developed an idea that decided his company to purchase hundreds of thousands of acres of land in the Permian basin. On this land production was found which helped make the name of Gulf one of the greatest in our industry's history.

Charles Gould, in addition to his many other achievements, went into the field in the Texas Panhandle and came back with a geologic report to his employers recommending the drilling of a well. This well led to the discovery of the vast Panhandle gas reserves.

The prolific Yates oil field — one of the richest in the nation — came "roaring in" 40 years ago west of the Pecos River in Texas. Here was an area where wildcatters — and geologists — had said that "there is no oil." However, there was a young man by the name of Frank Rinker Clark who thought otherwise. Even in the early 1920s, petroleum geologists were still the object of scorn, and a well witcher who located drilling sites with a sprig cut from a peach tree was considered to be more scientific and much smarter than a college upstart like Clark who hammered on rocks trying to find the right spot to drill for oil.

Clark's surface studies convinced him that the area was a favorable one for the accumulation of petroleum and it was his recommendation to The Ohio Oil Company — now Marathon Oil Company — that resulted in the discovery of this giant field. Contrary

to the opinion of the best minds of that day, Clark "stuck his neck out," supported his own convictions, and proved that oil could be found west of the Pecos River.

In each case, Higgins, the woodsman, and Belt, Gould, and Clark, the geologists, used their God-given right to think boldly — to think contrary to the everyday, run-of-the-mill type of mediocre thinking. They observed the earth; they understood what they observed; and they brought forth new discoveries, not only in energy but also in our science. By so doing, their names went down in history and up in the respect of their fellow men.

Today, the world consumes oil at a rate of approximately 30 million barrels a day. It has been said recently by economists that the 60-million-barrel day is now almost upon us. During the next 10 years, our industry will be required to find 55 billion barrels of oil and 300 trillion cubic feet of gas in the United States simply to maintain an adequate reserve position with the increased demand.

This will require us to utilize both all our heritage and to add much more to it; if we do not, we shall have considerable difficulty in meeting this tremendous challenge of the near future. Unless we think as creative and bold scientists, without fear of honest mistakes — and by so doing create new concepts — many of us here will live to see petroleum geology become as unacceptable as it was in its early founding years.

The one factor which the explorer must have to succeed is the strength of his convictions to take a chance.

I would like to make one more point. My friend, Frank Morgan, one of our great geologists, recently said to me that he can recall the time when a man first became a true, well-rounded geologist and later specialized to become a petroleum geologist. Frank continued his observation by pointing out that, when full courses in petroleum geology were established, many students by-passed the path of becoming a well-rounded geologist — instead they took the short route to a quick degree — in petroleum geology.

I heartily agree with Frank, and I might add that today matters are even worse. Petroleum geology specialization is reaching a ridiculous extreme in some university departments — with the result that many petroleum geologists are completely out of touch with the broad spectrum of geology, including the whole spectrum of petroleum geology.

The time has come, I believe, for us to return to the practice of being, first of all, true, well-rounded geologists. Today it is imperative that we know all aspects of our science. We must return to the role of the flexible, fully informed geologists who can answer any call, anywhere, at any time, for whatever reason. In my opinion, this is precisely what Walker meant when he lectured his students nearly two centuries ago. We must get back to the earth if we are to succeed in our objective of finding petroleum for the future.

The purpose of becoming well-rounded geologists is not to prepare ourselves for such disasters as those which came along in the late 1950s and early 1960s when oil companies, large and small, started firing or laying off geologists or transferring them to some other work, or retiring them years ahead of time. The real purpose is to broaden our outlook and provide us with the opportunity to develop ideas outside our own limited spheres of activity. I know that the value of a good petroleum geologist will rise in direct proportion to his ability to see, to comprehend, and to be a part of the whole landscape of geology.

I believe, also, that a good geologist should break out of his geological shell and observe what is going on in the world of industry, economics, politics, and civic affairs. He should not permit himself to remain isolated — an island unto himself. He will have to meet and know the people with whom he lives and works. By so doing he will be able to broaden his thinking and his understanding of all that exists in the world around him. He will then be able to absorb valuable ideas, to revitalize his own processes of thought, to gain courage to express himself, and to be able to withstand any crisis.

He should know his community, work with it to help build a hospital or a museum, to serve on a school board or a symphony orchestra committee, or to lead a fund drive, as well as to know something about the other segments of his own industry.

While improving his position economically and socially, however, let the petroleum geologist not lose sight of the geological heritage which was his for the taking, and which prepared him in the fundamentals of his profession. Let him realize that he does, after all, owe something for having it. Let him learn to be a good steward, not to hide his knowledge, but to expose it and let it grow so that the heritage he leaves to his successors may be even finer than that which he received. This is what he owes.

Although I have more than 2$^1/_2$ months remaining to finish my term, I want to express my deep appreciation for the opportunity you have given me to serve as your fiftieth president. It is a singular honor which I hold above any I have received or will receive in the future. I have tried my utmost to serve you well. Only time will measure the success of my endeavors. I would be well rewarded if somehow I have contributed one small item to the heritage which is ours to pass on to those who follow us.

References

American Petroleum Institute, 1961, History of petroleum engineering: Dallas, Tex., Am. Petroleum Inst. Div. Production, 1241 p.

Walker, John, 1779, *in* Lectures on geology, Harold W. Scott, ed.: 1966: Univ. Chicago Press, 280 p.

White, I. C., 1885, Geology of natural gas: Science, v. 5, June 26, p. 521–522.

White, I. C., 1892, The Mannington oil field and the history of its development: Geol. Soc. America Bull., v. 3, no. 4, p. 187–216.

John J. Amoruso

Career history
Born 1930

1952	B. S. degree, geology, Tufts College
1957	M. S. degree, geology, University of Michigan
1957–1969	Pan American Petroleum Corp.
1969–present	Independent geologist

My proudest accomplishment was:
My proudest accomplishment is having so many good friends throughout the geological profession, and being honored by them with election to the office of president of AAPG, AGI, SIPES, HGS, and GCAGS. I got to know them by being involved in the affairs of various geological organizations and working with them for the benefit and advancement of the science and profession of geology. If I had not been active, I would not have met a good many of them, and it would have been a great loss.

My biggest disappointment was:
The decline of oil and gas exploration, particularly in the domestic United States. The wildcatting spirit which made the United States a worldwide leader in petroleum exploration has largely disappeared. Oil and gas price volatility is no doubt the biggest reason, but another major factor is that many company managers and geologists no longer feel that "oil is first found in the minds of men." Instead, there is a feeling that unless every technology possible is exhausted, regardless of cost considerations, there can be no prospect. There seems to be an unwillingness to accept reasonable exploration risk without having a technological escape avenue on which to blame a failure.

Anecdotal story
First experiences seem to be the most memorable, and one of mine occurred while I was well-sitting for the first time during the summer of 1956. I had a summer job with Stanolind Oil and Gas Company in Oklahoma City, between terms of my master's degree at the University of Michigan. To learn something about well-sitting, I was sent to the field with Charles R. (Chuck) Noll as my mentor, to be indoctrinated on how to well-sit a drilling well. I was used to running samples from older wells, but not in real time. This was the first drilling well I had ever been on, so I knew little about operations. Chuck had the job of bringing me up to speed.

The well was located in southern Oklahoma near the town of Bokchito, close to the Red River. It was being drilled in conjunction with another company and was designed to penetrate the Ouachita thrust with as straight a hole as possible. We were watching the well in 12-hour tours with the other company. Because we were juniors, we had the night assignment. After a couple of days, Chuck was called back to Oklahoma City to relieve a geologist on another well, and I was on my own. The well was not challenging.

The temperatures stayed above 100 degrees day and night, and the well was drilling ahead at a dead-slow one hour 45 minutes per foot, in a seemingly unending dark gray orthoquartzite. It was a relief to get a five-foot sample. At about 2:00 a.m. one night, the roughneck opened the door of the small, un-air-conditioned trailer, said "Sample" to wake me up, and threw the sample bag onto the floor. Dutifully, I looked at it immediately and was shocked to wakefulness by the most beautiful oil show in a great-looking coarse, porous sandstone I had ever seen. I did all the tests to make sure the show was real — and it was.

Galvanized into action, I ran out to the rig and heard the brake squeaking away. I told the driller to circulate and highballed it into town to call my boss with what I thought was good news.

The boss was less than pleased at being awakened, and when I told him we had five feet of this show, he was not at all as enthusiastic as I was. He told me to go back to the rig and call him back if we had 20 more feet of the sand. I never saw the sand or the apparent drilling break again. The well continued to drill at the old rate of one hour 45 minutes per foot in the same old lithology.

I was convinced that the sample had been salted from some other, very good oil well, but I was careful not to bring up that possibility with the crew. Things had been pretty dull as the well ground endlessly down without change, and some excitement would have been appreciated. "Let's see what kind of rise we can get out of that weevil geologist" was probably the motivation. It worked, and I took the bait, hook, line, and sinker. Nevertheless, I am consoled by the fact that I erred on the side of safety.

Since the first well, I have seen a goodly number of shows, but none that seemed as good as I remember this one. I don't know where it came from, but I've been looking for one just like it ever since. Maybe someday I will find another show as good, and if I do, I will make sure it isn't a trick.

My advice to you is:
Be involved in the affairs of professional societies and give back something to your profession. Keep your professional expertise up to date by taking advantage of educational opportunities afforded by professional organizations. Use this broadened education with your work experience to be a more complete geologist and a better oil and gas finder.

Philip F. Anschutz

Career history
Born 1939

1961	B.A. degree in business, University of Kansas
1961–1965	Worked for my father, Fred Anschutz, an independent oil and gas operator based in Wichita, Kansas, and Denver, Colorado
1965–present	Self-employed, the Anschutz Corporation

My proudest accomplishments to date include the following:
My proudest accomplishment was starting up a business as a young man, and having it thrive in an industry that is not particularly forgiving of either inexperience or youthful start-ups and which can, and often does, punish mistakes severely. To be a small independent in a business that is high-risk, cyclical, and habitually short of capital was scary at times, breathtaking at others, but rewarding most of the time.

My biggest disappointment
My biggest disappointment was the Utah/Wyoming Overthrust Play. Although it was certainly successful, it just did not extend as far north or south as I might have wished, and where, regrettably, much of the additional acreage I had leased was located. The thinking that the acreage was on trend, which it was, was correct. Regrettably, the thinking concerning tectonics, timing, and reservoirs was not.

Anecdotal story
An incident that has always had a great effect and impact on me in later years is one that began when I was awakened from a sound sleep in the middle of the night by a phone call from the tool pusher of a rig I owned which was drilling a rank wildcat outside Gillette, Wyoming. He informed me that we had experienced a blowout during the night, and the well was out of control.

I remember thinking, "Is this a disaster or an opportunity?" and almost turning the light out, going back to sleep, and lamenting my bad luck. Instead, I called the airport, hired a small plane, and flew to Gillette as quickly as possible, arriving at sunup. I managed to borrow a car from the airport manager and drove to the rig to see what was happening. The well was clearly out of control, with oil spraying over the crown block of the rig at an estimated minimum rate of 10,000 barrels per day.

By noon, I had sent lease crews into the field to lease

acreage on trend and on 30-day drafts. I had contacted Red Adair about capping the well and had contacted the insurance company and the offset lease owners, as well as the other interest holders in the well.

By late that evening, a Halliburton pump truck had come on location with an open engine stack and had sparked the gas, which eventually exploded, setting fire to the rig and the pools of oil around the rig, but fortunately not causing any loss of life.

By the following day, the offset lease owners and landowners had sued for damages, the insurance company had refused to honor the coverage, and Red Adair had refused to take the job of extinguishing the fire and capping the well unless I paid a large up-front deposit. The only good news was that the lease crews had been successful in leasing acreage on trend, but even that carried the bad news that I had only 30 days to pay to cover the drafts and had no money with which to do so. This of course was the same problem that Red Adair had recognized — hence his reluctance to take a job unless he had an up-front payment.

Facing the uncertainties of a major blowout, and lack of money and other financial resources to succeed, it looked like a recipe for disaster — not to mention that at that point, at least technically, I was bankrupt.

The story, however, had a happy ending. I quickly sold the film rights to a Hollywood studio (footage was used in *Hellfighters — the Red Adair Story*). I negotiated to take over full liability for putting out the fire in return for a larger interest in the well and its surrounding acreage. I made a quick sale of an interest in the trend acreage I was purchasing. I successfully defended against the reservoir damage claims by offset lease holders and settled with the insurance company. By using the proceeds from the movie company and the sale of interest in the trend acreage, I was able to pay Red Adair a deposit and to film him putting the fire out. I also settled the costs associated with the blowout and cleanup, and met my 30-day draft obligations on the new acreage.

All of this taught me, at the young age of 26, that it is often difficult to distinguish between a problem and an opportunity, that quick and decisive action normally pays huge dividends, and that nothing much of value is ever obtained without exposing oneself to large risks and suffering the added insult of both stupidity and failure if things don't work out as planned.

The field that was discovered by that blowout was the Kitty Field, and it led to a string of other discoveries in the Muddy Play of the 1960s in the Powder River Basin.

Admittedly, in this case I was lucky, but it was a series of events and decisions that has had a profound long-term effect on me throughout my business career.

My advice

That portion of the oil business which is best defined as being "an independent oil and gas operator" is certainly considered to be a high-risk endeavor. These risks can be mitigated by the normal things — hard work, plenty of preparation, surrounding yourself with people who are smarter than you, and a normal portion of leadership skills. But at the end of the day, remember this — most things you do will fail, and psychologically, you must be mentally prepared for it. It is simply a matter of statistics. There will be a lot more dry wells than there ever will be productive wells. The most important advice I can give you is this: Always remember it is not failure that keeps people from accomplishing great things. It is the fear of failure that stops them.

Bruce Appelbaum

Career history
Born 1947

1969	B.A., geological sciences, SUNY/Buffalo
1971	M.S., geological oceanography, Texas A&M University
1974	Ph.D., geological oceanography, Texas A&M University
1974–1977	Sun Oil Company
1977–1978	Superior Oil
	Gulf of Suez: Alma Field
1978–1981	Texas Eastern Exploration
1981–1984	SEDCO Energy
1984–1989	Champlin/Union Pacific Resources
	Gulf of Mexico H.I. 178
1989–2002	Texaco, Inc.
	Nigeria: Agbami, Nnwa, Aparo
	Brazil: BS-4
	Trinidad: Dolphin Deep, Starfish
	Gulf of Mexico: Petronius, Champlain, Tahiti
	Partitioned Neutral Zone: Humma

My proudest accomplishments
- Raising a productive, healthy family.

- Successfully participating in the opening of the deep-water Gulf, Nigeria, and Brazil.

- My career highlight was unquestionably my tenure at Texaco, when I was hired as offshore Gulf of Mexico exploration manager and retired as a corporate vice president and president of worldwide exploration and new ventures. Groups under my direction found 3 billion barrels of oil equivalent in a four-year time frame, all in an ultraconservative environment. The company had endured years of exploration failure and monetary waste prior to our success.

My biggest disappointment
Watching the continuous downsizing of the oil and gas business.

Anecdotal story
My anecdotal story concerns my interview process and the value of persistence when you are convinced that you are correct. During a series of preemployment research interviews in 1989, I was asked generally about my exploration philosophy and views toward improving Texaco's position relative to its peer companies. I waxed enthusiastic about the importance of petroleum systems and technological advances. I explained the coming importance of deep-water exploration, at which point I was stopped cold and told categorically, "Texaco does not do deep water."

I found this to be a curious statement and probed for the reasons. All were related to emotions following initial failures rather than to hard data and sound science. I accepted the viewpoint and accepted the job, but was fully determined that it was up to me to move the company outside its narrow view if it was to succeed in changing its results. The company had excellent people and resources but was limited in its vision.

My most important task was establishing a drilling portfolio, quantifying its risk, and translating the probable outcome to an upper organization that was accustomed to failure.

Many trips to White Plains and a sound plan produced the proper result. During the process, however, numerous memos were sent to our office, outlining the success of others. This only served to strengthen our resolve. Our persistence was rewarded, but it took four years of patience to acquire high-grade risk and execute the portfolio, which vindicated our plan. The company was initially stunned (confused) by our success. In fact, there was great reluctance initially to ask for funds to delineate our initial successes. Asking for more money in any context seemed to be viewed as fiscal irresponsibility, even if it was meant to confirm a success!

It takes great fortitude to change a culture. All of the foregoing highlights the need for persistence to accomplish anything, in this business or any other.

My advice
Do what you enjoy and be persistent. Keep learning!

Acknowledgments
I am indebted to many individuals who helped to guide my path through academia and my professional career. I feel a kinship with all earth scientists, but a special few provided the mentoring and inspiration that deserve special thanks.

In particular, I want to recognize Arnold Bouma, Bill Bryant, and Dick Rezak for their help during my years in graduate school at Texas A&M's Oceanography Department.

Three special individuals from my professional career are acknowledged as well. All three taught me that success can coexist with humanity, and that character is the most important attribute in any career. The first two are Fred Christian and Phil Raveling, both deceased and sorely missed. The third is Bill Wallace, a friend and true leader.

Robert J. Ardell

Career history

1940	Born in Hinsdale, Illinois
1962	B.A. degree from Monmouth College, Monmouth, Illinois, in geology/economics
1965	M.S. degree from Kansas State University, Manhattan, Kansas, in geology
1965–1971	Union Oil Company of California, Houston and New Orleans
1971–1974	Clark Oil Producing Company, New Orleans and Houston
1974–1977	Kerr-McGee Corp., Houston
1977–1990	Samedan Oil Corporation (Noble Energy), Houston
1990–2002	Nippon Oil Exploration USA Limited, Houston

My proudest accomplishments to date include the following:

Professionally, I suppose I am proudest of having the desire and ability to practice the unconventional. For example, in 1977, I left a perfectly good and promising regional manager's job at Kerr-McGee Corp. to strike out on a plan, as a consultant, to initiate and farm out acreage from the majors in the Gulf of Mexico and cause drilling by Samedan and others on these ideas. Although farm-out activity had long been common in the Gulf of Mexico, never had a program been established by one person as a growth plan for a company. With the incentive of an override, the project of getting Samedan growing in the Gulf of Mexico was quite successful.

After my 13-year tenure at Samedan, most of the low fruit seemed to have been harvested on the Gulf of Mexico shelf. Clearly, many new discoveries have been made in recent years and new technology has helped to maintain reasonable success ratios, but reserve size has been a problem.

Feeling that the earth was becoming smaller and smaller with rapidly improving technology and communication, I chose to move to a more global-scale project. Nippon Oil, the largest Japanese oil-refining company, expressed a desire to make an attempt at establishing itself in the western hemisphere as an upstream entity. I decided to join in this effort and organized, staffed, and slowly built a "small American independent," Nippon Oil Exploration USA Limited.

This was a significant effort for me and for the Japanese, and a challenging one in light of the stagnant Japanese economy of the 1990s as well as the profound cultural differences between East and West. The U.S. affiliate established many firsts for the company and is now a profitable organization contributing to the corporate balance sheet.

NOEX USA manages interests in the Syncrude project in Canada as well as projects in Venezuela, the U.S. Gulf of Mexico shelf and deep water, and onshore Texas.

Both the Samedan and Nippon projects required unconventional thinking and personal initiative, and both projects provided a feeling of accomplishment for me.

My biggest disappointment is really difficult to determine.

Enjoying my work and creating wealth for many people make any business disappointments seem insignificant. I can't really say I have had "a biggest professional disappointment."

Anecdotal story

Like most people whose histories are included in this book, I have anecdotal stories about trying to sell a deal 20+ times only to drill it without partners and (1) finding a large gas field and (2) drilling a dry hole. I also have stories about not quitting on a deep, expensive wildcat, with similar mixed results. One project stands out as a spectacular success for my company. After drilling in a very tough environment in Eugene Island with several sidetracks and terrible cost overruns, we drilled ahead and found a 200-BCF field! But to add balance, I remember a deep well in Main Pass that only got worse, and the deeper we drilled, the more the cost overruns accumulated.

I have to say my story might be the story of "my proudest accomplishment." Don't be afraid of moving away from the herd if you feel you have thought through the options. Some of life's greatest opportunities and most stimulating challenges lie over the hill just beyond the horizon. Failure might result, but it is seldom fatal. Some level of risk stimulates everyone.

My history of moving from large company to small independent to large company to independent to an Asian bureaucracy as difficult as any represents my idea of challenge and growth. This diet of change has stimulated me in my work and productivity. Regular repotting within the organization or without should improve your contribution to the industry.

My advice

Be open to new opportunities and new ideas. Maintain a satisfactory skill level, which is no small task with the rapid changes in our industry. Practice the highest ethical principles, and have fun. People who enjoy their work do good work. If work ceases to be fun, move on to something or someplace different.

Enjoy and learn from your fellow professionals. You are fortunate to be working with perhaps the best comrades in any industry.

Acknowledgments

No one travels far in this business without support and help along the way. Many could be acknowledged, and here are just a few: Atake, Barclay, Beck, Hooker, Jobe, Mcgee, McKenny, McLeod, Moore, Noble, Ratcliff, Skelly, So, Wills . . . and others have profoundly influenced my professional life either through philosophy, education, or facilitating and supporting my efforts. Little is possible without support, mentoring, wise counsel, and advice.

My apologies to the many I have omitted.

William J. Barrett

Cherry Hills Village, Colorado

Career history

Born January 9, 1929

1956	B.S. in geology, Kansas State University
1958	M.S. in geology, Kansas State University
1958	El Paso Natural Gas stratigrapher, Research Lab, Rocky Mountains
1962	Pan American (Amoco) project geologist, Rocky Mountains
1966	Wolf Exploration/INEXCO, chief geologist, Rocky Mountains, part of a team that discovered a 4+ TCF Maddon Field, Wind River Basin, Wyoming, and 200+ million BOE Hilight Field Complex, Powder River Basin, Wyoming
1969	B & C Exploration, president/partner, consultant
1970	Rainbow Resources, vice president; exploration manager, director, part of a team that discovered Red Wing Creek, Centennial, acquired, developed Medicine Pole Hills/Coyote Creek, other fields in Williston Basin, North Dakota, 4 MM gross acres under lease in the Rocky Mountains
1978	Sold Rainbow Resources Corp. to the Williams Companies of Tulsa, Oklahoma
1978	Sole proprietor, 200+ BCFE field extension of Wattenberg Field, D-J Basin, Colorado
1981	Barrett Energy Company, private,

founder, chief executive officer, chairman, exploration geologist

1983	Barrett Resources Corp., public, NASDAQ, NYSE (1994), president, chief executive officer, chairman, exploration geologist
	Discovered and developed 1.2-TCF Parachute–Grand Valley–Rulison Field ult. ± 4TC gas field, Piceance Basin, Colorado
	Discovered and developed 500-BCFE Cave Gulch Field, Wind River Basin, Wyoming
	Developed 4+TCF Powder River Basin coalbed methane development, Powder River Basin, Wyoming
	IP Barrett Resources Corp. was sold to the Williams Companies of Tulsa in a transaction valued at $2.8 billion
2001	Traveled extensively worldwide
2002	Formed Bill Barrett Corp., private E&P company with focus on the Rocky Mountains; chief executive officer, chairman

A few of my proudest accomplishments were:

One of my proudest accomplishments was being involved with successful companies such as El Paso, Pan American/Amoco, INEXCO, and Rainbow, culminating with formation of and growth of Barrett Resources Corp. from 1981 to August 3, 2001, when the company was sold to Williams Companies, Inc.

Historical track record of Barrett Resources Corp.

Company	Private ('81–'83)	NASDAQ ('83–'94) NYSE ('94–'01)
Employees	7	265
Daily production	0	341 mmcfe/d
Proven reserves	0	2.1 tcfe (8 TCF probable, possible)
Capital budget	0	$423 MM
Stock value	$0.38	$ 73.32/share

Another accomplishment was being a key part of several exploration teams that discovered and developed five giant or near giant oil and gas fields and numerous other smaller oil and gas fields in the Rockies. I was proud of participating in true company-maker projects.

In 2002, at age 73, I jointly formed Bill Barrett Corporation, a new Rocky Mountain E&P company, with several of my prior colleagues and raised $282 MM of private equity start-up capital.

My biggest disappointments were:

I have not had much disappointment — lots of ups and downs with pricing, and onerous environmental and regulatory requirements, but that's the way of doing business today.

One disappointment occurred in 1986, when oil and gas prices dropped and we had to downsize. This was the only time it happened. It was a difficult and very unpleasant experience.

Experiences in drilling dry holes on very high profile, "can't-miss" prospects were all big disappointments at the time, but as an explorationist, you drill dry holes, learn, and move on.

The Cave Gulch 1-29 blowout flowed more than 100 MMCFG per day for months. The rig burned down, and we lost an estimated 20 BCF gas while getting the well under control. The good news was that no one got hurt.

An anecdotal story

There are so many stories in my 45-year career that it is difficult to select one. Barrett Resources Corporation was well known for its success in the Piceance Basin. In 1983, when we first started to assemble this project, the area was considered to have very poor to no potential by most people in the industry. In their view, the basin had very poor, tight, reservoir rock and lots of shows, most of the production was marginal, terrain was rough, costs were high, gas markets were poor, etc. The Piceance was simply considered to be a very poor place to explore for and develop hydrocarbons.

I had previously had the opportunity to work in most of the Rocky Mountain basins. I saw the Piceance as a virtually unexplored basin with a large gas-saturated Cretaceous section. Rocks of the same age were commercially productive in all of the surrounding basins. For many years, the central portion of the basin was not drilled because of oil shale development. I recognized the possible potential for a basin-centered gas trap similar to the prolific San Juan Basin Fields to the south.

In 1983, we proceeded in assembling a 45,000-acre lease position with no competition and drilled an initial five exploratory wells. Four wells were successful. With the help of new massive frac technology, we proceeded to develop the now 2+ TCF Parachute–Grand Valley–Rulison gas-producing complex. By July 2002, this complex was producing approximately 160 MMCFGE from 400+ wells with an ongoing five-well drilling program.

My advice to you:

The oil and gas exploration and production business is an exciting profession where you, individually, can make a difference. There is none like it. The people you work with are the best you can find anywhere.

Become an expert in your field, focus on your area of expertise, rely on your own geology, draw your own conclusions, think outside the box, utilize all the new available technology, be optimistic.

Look for new opportunities — they are out there. Grow via the drill bit — it's more fun than acquisitions. Enjoy your work, and have fun!

Once you achieve experience, don't be afraid to do your own thing.

Richard S. Bishop

Career history
Born 1945

1967	B.S. in geology, Texas Christian University
1969	M.A. in geology, University of Missouri, Columbia
1969–1971	Development geologist, Union Oil Co. of California
1974	Ph.D. in geology, Stanford University
1975–present	Exxon in its many forms
1975–1981	Exxon Production Research Co.
1981–1984	Exxon USA Exploration
1984–1986	Exxon USA Production
1986–1992	Esso Exploration/ Exxon Production Research
1992–present	Exxon/ExxonMobil Exploration Co.

My most significant accomplishment was:
Recognizing that traps are full to either a leak point or spillpoint. The implications were several, e.g., (1) it opened the field of secondary migration and showed that we must evaluate prospects on the basis of leaks, (2) it added another control of gas versus oil (i.e., gas displacement of oil), and (3) it showed that source-rock productivity overwhelmed trap capacity and that prediction of trapped volumes required one to find the smaller of source-rock productivity or trap capacity. It changed the way we mapped and risked prospects.

This discovery was made independently of but after Shell discovered the same/similar thing.

My biggest disappointment was:

Nothing really comes to mind … but I am still chagrined about a 1982 farmout of some acreage in the offshore Texas state waters. I was new in the job and simply went along with what was on the books — the prospect was too small for us. In reality, it was not risked properly, compared to our drillable prospects. At that time, we did not appreciate the difference in chance of success of a (small) four-way closure versus a (very large) fault trap.

Anecdotal story

My biggest kick of discovery occurred by explaining some well-known observations quite differently than in the past. This meant that some widely used concepts — or perhaps presumptions — were not correct. Arriving at these conclusions, however, was not straightforward and not without doubt, and presenting them was not without pain. I learned that altering presumptions is hard. Folks who had used the established concepts in their exploration habits did not seize on change with open arms.

Early in my Exxon career, I was part of a group responsible for building various yardsticks to increase consistency in prospect assessments from all over the world. My task was to develop a yardstick on percent trap fill. At that time, it was thought that most prospects were underfilled and that source-rock productivity limited the amount of trapped hydrocarbons. Some traps were full to spill, but such full traps were thought to be the exception, not the rule. Furthermore, at that time, we did not know what controlled gas/oil, oil/water, or gas/water contacts.

A different way to look at the question was to measure fill in three dimensions. Prior workers generally had few detailed field maps, and percent trap fill commonly meant a 2-D ratio of field area to the synclinal area. Looking in 3-D required one to find the detailed field maps and, if possible, to identify what controlled the location of the hydrocarbon contact.

This I did. I looked at hundreds of fields in 3-D and discovered that hydrocarbon contacts commonly coincided with the syncline and also were especially common with reservoir-to-reservoir contacts (now commonly called cross-fault leakage).

The implications were significant to both prospect mapping and to predicting oil versus gas. It meant that the limit of trap fill was not source-rock productivity but trap integrity, which meant that we had to assess prospects in three dimensions rather than two. In addition, it meant that source-rock productivity typically overwhelmed trap capacity rather than limiting the amount of trapped hydrocarbon. There was a corollary that meant gas displacement of oil was an important control in predicting oil versus gas. This expanded our tools in predicting oil versus gas beyond LOM and source-rock type to include volumetrics of productivity and trap volume.

I was fortunate to work with some outstanding scientists, especially Al Young and Dave White. Al was the geochemist who developed the source-rock yield and LOM models, and Dave was the lead assessor. As the data came in, I would plot them up, stew on them a while, and then talk to Al. We would have marvelous dialogues about the meaning of it all. When it came time to report to Dave, he recognized and appreciated the major change in the conceptual basis for much exploration, but also recognized that it meant major changes to the way we assessed prospects.

My advice to you is:

Wise persons can tell the difference between advice and personal opinion. I generally try not to give advice — folks usually know what they want to do or ought to do.

Try to ask questions differently or do data acquisition differently than has been done previously.

Acknowledgments

The key influences in my career were twofold: One influenced my process of thinking, and the other changed my career responsibilities. Neither taught me tools of how to do something but, unknown to them, these folks changed the way I thought about and did things. It is helpful to me to name them.

In terms of career influence, Mike Johnson of ExxonMobil, John Harbaugh of Stanford University, and Bill Bishop (no relation, but a past president of the Houston Geological Society) provided support at decision points in my career. Mike, John, and Bill all know, and are greatly appreciated for, the roles they played in influencing my career.

In terms of problem solving, the folks who left a lasting impression are Al Young at Exxon Production Research Company and Jim Lewis, past president AAPG. Both listened and listened and listened, asked a few questions, and said a few words which led me to the great "Ahhhaaa! I've got it!" event.

Daniel A. Busch

Petroleum consultant, Tulsa, Oklahoma

Career history
Born 1912

1934	B.S. degree in chemistry, Capital University
1936	M.A. degree in geology, Ohio State University
1939	Ph.D. degree in geology, Ohio State University
1938:	Instructor of geology, University of Pittsburgh
1942	Geologist, Pennsylvania Geological Survey
1943	Consulting geologist, Huntley & Huntley
1946	Senior research geologist, Carter Research Laboratory
1949	Staff geologist, Carter Oil Co.
1951	Exploration manager, Zephyr Petroleum Co.
1954–1992	Consulting geologist

Part-time teaching positions, visiting professor, University of Tulsa, Oil and Gas Consultants, International

My proudest accomplishment was:
Numerous oil and gas discoveries in Ohio, Oklahoma, eastern Kansas, the Rocky Mountains, and Mexico, and receiving the Sidney Powers Gold Medal

My biggest disappointment was:
Neither of my two sons chose geology for a career.

An anecdotal story
I generated a "hot" prospect for oil and gas, sat on the well continuously for three days and nights, and had to plug it as a dry hole. When I reached home at 3 a.m., it was necessary to awaken my wife to unlock the front door. After she greeted me with a kiss, I asked her if she might be interested in knowing the outcome of the drilling of my favorite prospect. She replied in the affirmative, and I replied, "It was a dry hole!" Her reply was simply, "Better luck next time." Because there was no expression of sympathy for my failure, I then posed the following question. "Do you realize you could have replaced every piece of furniture and carpeting in our home with new furnishings with the amount of money I spent on my working interest in that dry hole?" Her reply was, "You will do better next time."

My advice to you is:
Geology students who intend to pursue a career in petroleum exploration should complete one or two years of graduate studies in geology and geophysics before seeking employment. After several years of employment they should periodically enroll in special courses, such as those sponsored by the AAPG and the industry. This is the most effective means of succeeding in a highly competitive industry.

A. T. (Toby) Carleton

Midland, Texas

Career history

Born March 5, 1929, Houston, Texas

1951	B.S. degree in geology, University of Texas at Austin
1952	M.A. degree in geology, University of Texas at Austin
1952–1955	The Ohio Oil Company (now Marathon), Midland, Texas, and Roswell, New Mexico
1955–1961	Zapata Petroleum Corporation, Midland, Texas, chief geologist
1961–1963	Independent geologist, Midland, Texas
1963–1976	Structurmaps, Ltd., Midland, Texas, general partner
1976–1979	Independent geologist, Midland, Texas
1979–1989	Pogo Producing Company, Midland, Texas, vice president
1989–1991	Tocor Exploration (representing Energy Exploration Management on contract to Canadian Hunter Exploration, Ltd.)
1991–present	Tocor Investments, Inc., and Tocor Exploration, Midland, Texas, president; Imperial Operating Company, LLC, Midland, Texas, member

My proudest accomplishment was:

My proudest accomplishments have to do with the professional societies that I have served, at the local, national, and international levels. I have been president of West Texas Geological Society, chairman of the Midland Chapter of SIPES, chairman of the AAPG House of Delegates, president of SIPES, and president of AAPG. Although I have been at least partly responsible for several oil and gas discoveries and developments, the contacts and networking that I made through these professional organizations are the things that have been most important to me in my career.

It is through these associations that I have met people from all over the world who are not only my friends, but have in many cases contributed to whatever successes I may have achieved.

My biggest disappointment was:

My biggest disappointment occurred fairly early in my career. I was fired from a job that I really liked. I was so devastated that I stayed in bed for three days. This, however, turned out to be the best possible thing that could have happened to me. It strengthened my resolve and focused my direction. Had I not been forced to go out on my own in a time of high unemployment in our industry, I would probably, at best, have retired as a staff geologist for a medium-sized oil company.

As it was, I was forced into becoming an entrepreneur, formed several successful businesses, consulted for multimillion-dollar companies, became vice president of a large aggressive independent exploration company, and am currently dividing my time between the oil and gas business and ranching. I am content with my position in life.

An anecdotal story

Back in the early 1960s, I turned a deal which resulted in a good Devonian gas discovery. There was, however, no market for the gas at that time in that place. Subsequently, things got really bad for me and I wasn't sure I was going to survive in this business. My wife and small children had gone to visit her parents for the Christmas holidays. I was to join them on New Year's Eve. I had already decided that I must tell my wife that we were going to have to find another way of making a living.

On New Year's Eve, I got a call from Bill Liedtke, who was to become president of the Pennzoil Company, which was then being formed. They were acquiring various entities to put into the new company, and were looking to purchase properties for this purpose before the end of that year. Bill asked if I still had my interest in the shut-in gas well. As it turned out, they bought my interest in that well for several thousand dollars. It bailed me out and allowed me to continue in the business that I love. It was also the best New Year's Eve that I ever had.

As a side note, I saved out some of the acreage on

this prospect, which later proved to be productive also. I am still receiving income from this prospect more than 40 years later.

My advice to you is:

My advice to anyone not already so doing is to get involved in your professional society at any level. In addition to the contacts and networking referred to earlier, the continuing educational opportunities offered by all these organizations afford the geoscientist the avenue to stay abreast of technological advances.

Another word of advice is to be persistent. Don't give up. Sometimes it is darkest right before the dawn. That is the moral of my anecdotal story.

Acknowledgments

Many people have had a positive influence on my professional career. A few of those I would like to acknowledge are listed here. George H. W. Bush and Hugh Liedtke, at Zapata Petroleum Corporation, taught me the business side of the oil business. Bill Liedtke not only saved my career, but was a guiding influence in it. Bill Gipson was my boss and mentor and has been my friend for more than 50 years. Harry Miller has been my friend and has helped me to survive during tough times. Bruno Hanson was my mentor and my dear friend. My wife, Corinne, has stood by me and encouraged me "for better or for worse" for the last 50 years.

Robey H. Clark

Geologist, Amarillo, Texas

Career history

Born 1921, Mound, Madison Parish, Louisiana

1943	B.S. degree in geology, Louisiana State University
1943–1946	U.S. Navy, Pacific Theater, served on LSTs 220, 242, 451
1946–1947	Geologist, Magnolia Petroleum Co., Oklahoma and New Mexico
1948	Married Marjorie Joanne Justus; four children, seven grandchildren
1949	M.S. degree in geology, University of Wisconsin at Madison
1949–1971	Magnolia Petroleum Co. and its parent, Mobil Oil Corp., Gulf Coast, Midcontinent, Rocky Mountains, etc.
1971–1982	Diamond Shamrock Corp., Amarillo, Texas (all of the United States plus the North Sea and marine areas of Australia and New Zealand)
1982–1990	Independent consultant, various clients
1992–present	Over-the-hill bystander interested in sources of energy to year 2100 attempts to reclaim our nation from the bureaucracy.

AAPG secretary, 1977–1979; president, 1980-1981; honorary member, 1985; member DPA, EMD, DEG

My proudest accomplishment was:
Successful association with Gulf of Mexico offshore, 1948–1982.

My biggest disappointment was:
The merger craze.

An anecdotal story

In March 1943, when I was two months shy of graduation at LSU, the U.S. Navy called me into service. In September 1943, I went to war on an LST in the Pacific.

In March 1946, I debarked in San Francisco. While awaiting transportation to Louisiana, I applied for work at Standard Oil of California. A vice president interviewed me. At the close, he said he could offer me an entry-level job, but added that Standard of California was clannish, and promotion was slow for geologists from schools outside the West Coast. He suggested I go home and look for work in the Gulf Coast, and if that failed, get back to him. I was pleased, but puzzled by "Yes, we have an opening, but you wouldn't like it." It was my first lukewarm welcome.

Back in Louisiana, I borrowed a car and headed west on U.S. 80. While still miles from Dallas, I spotted the red Pegasus atop the Magnolia building. The next day, I knocked on Magnolia's door. Soon I was received by a high-ranking exploration executive — the first of several in a long day of interviews. At day's end, they said Magnolia would like to hire me, but they had to consider former employees still in service. They suggested I interview in the busy city of Tulsa, Oklahoma, and if nothing turned up, come back to see them. Puzzled at my second lukewarm welcome, I drove to Tulsa.

At nine next morning, I called on Sinclair Oil. A soft-spoken, elderly gentleman interviewed me at some length. He said he would like to have me in Sinclair but suggested that I try elsewhere, and if nothing turned up, come back to see him. Disappointed, I asked why he preferred that I work for someone else. I was startled and puzzled to hear him imply that I might not feel comfortable in the business culture at Sinclair. He did not elaborate. It was a lukewarm welcome with a twist.

I applied at Carter Oil. Its vice president was a truly large man with a hearty manner and a booming voice.

After some talk, he asked if I drank whiskey. Very carefully, I said, "Well, yes — sometimes — a little."

"That's good to know," he said. "It's a funny thing, but I just can't really trust a man that won't take a drink." In due course, he said he could offer me a job on a geophysical crew, but it wouldn't be ready for a month or two, so try elsewhere and check back in a few weeks … another lukewarm welcome.

At Skelly, I interviewed with a quiet, scholarly gentleman who said they would be starting a surface geology field party in about a month and he could put me on at a beginner's wage. If I was interested, he would call me when the work began. It was yet another iffy lukewarm welcome. I tried a couple of more companies and gave up.

I returned to Dallas and went back to Magnolia. Glory be! They actually hired me at about $225 a month and assigned me to Oklahoma City. When I reported on May 1, 1946, district geologist Dr. Walt Moreman said I was just in time to change to field clothes and go sit on a well with an ex-navy guy named Ken Keller.

Many years later, I asked Dr. Henry Cortes, one of the Magnolia executives who interviewed me, why they had offered me a job. He reminded me that on the application, there had been a question asking what I hoped to accomplish in the next two years. My answer was to get a good job and get a wife. Cortes then asked if I had a girl. I answered, "Not yet." Cortes liked my answer. He said he figured I'd be good at setting worthy goals and making good things happen. Anyway, Magnolia and I had 25 good years together … and I still have the girl!

My advice to you is:
Just do the right thing.

Acknowledgments

In my career, I am indebted to a host of geologists and nongeologists, but two stand out — Carlos Ferguson, who patiently helped me return to civilian life as a geologist in 1946, and Philip Jennings, who taught me a sense of scale in exploration, and the enormity of exploration and producing potential in the Gulf of Mexico and all over the world.

Robert D. (Bob) Cowdery

Consulting geologist, Wichita, Kansas

Career history
Born August 20, 1926, Lyons, Kansas

1944–1946	Military justice specialist, technical sergeant
1946–1949	B.S. in physical science, geology major, Kansas State University
	Additional coursework, Denver University, University of Colorado, Colorado School of Mines, and Wichita State University (230 hours total credit)
1949–1951	Geologist, Cities Service Oil Co., Oklahoma City, Oklahoma, and Great Bend, Kansas
1951–1988	Petroleum, Inc.
1951–1953	Staff geologist, Wichita, Kansas
1953–1956	District geologist, Denver, Colorado
1956–1967	Division geologist, Denver, Colorado
1967–1975	Rocky Mountain exploration manager, vice president, Denver; explored in all major basins of the Rocky Mountains (United States) plus Canada
1975–1985	Exploration manager, vice president, Wichita, Kansas; responsible for exploration in 11 states
1985–1986	Executive vice president, chief operating officer
1986–1988	President, chief operating officer
1988	Director of exploration
1988–present	Consulting geologist, Wichita, Kansas

Accomplishments
I commenced martial-arts training when I was 42 years old and have continued to the present. My proudest accomplishment is achieving the rank of Sixth Dan (sixth-degree) black belt and remaining active at the age of 75 years — this despite the fact that my athletic ability is limited.

My biggest disappointments were:
Even though I continued my education for a long period after receiving my B.S. degree, I did not persevere to the point of obtaining any advanced degrees, although I had 59 hours of anthropology and 39 hours toward an M.B.A.

I failed to find nearly enough reserves of oil and gas for my company with the high number of exploratory tests that the company drilled.

An anecdotal story
My story deals with an example taken from a presentation that I make, called "Mistakes I Have Made." Our company secured a half interest (later increased to a three-quarter interest) in a prospect in Renville County, North Dakota. The exploratory technique was simple. We drilled in an indicated updip direction from an abandoned test with extremely good shows of oil, but it had been overperforated and produced water. After the discovery, we drilled some excellent development wells (many of these wells have subsequently made more than 1 million barrels of oil apiece).

As the field developed, I prided myself on understanding the trapping mechanism, which was a facies change from a porous limestone to an argillaceous zone across a structural nose. What I didn't realize was that this was a very complex depositional and structural area, possibly involving two episodes of salt collapse. On the other side of my perfect barrier were two more fields just as good as the first one. These fields straddled the border with Canada, and our company had only one producer in the two fields.

Downdip from our discovery was a lease on which the company had moved a rig and was preparing to spud. I had the location abandoned because I thought the test to be drilled would encounter the Sherwood (Frobisher-Alida) pay zone below the oil-water contact. What I didn't realize was that the 29-gravity oil had been tilted because of the hydrodynamics of the area downdip. The operator who later drilled the lease obtained two excellent wells. These mistakes all resulted from my being "too damn smart" and thinking I understood the geology when I didn't.

My advice to you is:
If you are a practicing geologist, stay with what you

are doing. I write profiles on geologists more than 70 years of age. I have written more than 80 of these profiles. One question I ask is, "If you had it to do over, would you still be a petroleum geologist?" With possibly one exception, they have all said, "Why, certainly, there isn't anything better than this" or words to that effect.

To the student or newly graduated geologist entering the field, I would say, "Don't get 'too damn smart' — you may not have all the answers."

Marlan W. Downey

Career history
Born 1932, Falls City, Nebraska

1952	B.A. degree in chemistry, Peru State College
1952–1954	U.S. Army service in Korea
1954–1957	B.S. and M.S. degrees in geology, University of Nebraska
1957–1987	Shell Oil Company
1963–1967	Project manager, research, origin and migration of hydrocarbons, Shell Development
1967–1973	Chief geologist, western region
1973–1977	Alaska Division, exploration manager
1977–1979	Vice president, international exploration
1979–1987	President, Pecten International; retired 1987
1987–1990	Formed Roxanna Oil, consulted and explored worldwide
1990–1996	Arco International, senior vice president of exploration, president; exploration adviser to the Arco board; retired 1996
1996–2000	Bartell Professor and Chief Scientist, Sarkeys Energy Center, University of Oklahoma
2000–2001	President of AAPG
2001–present	Senior Fellow at the Institute for the Study of Earth and Man, Southern Methodist University, Dallas

Summary: I supervised exploration and development investments in 62 countries. Teams found and developed commercial fields in 20 countries. Six countries yielded more than 1 billion barrels equivalent.

I organized and chaired the first Hedberg Conference on "Seals for Hydrocarbons" in 1984, the first Hedberg Conference on "Understanding Risk in E and P" in 1993, the fifth conference on "Unconventional Methods of Exploration" in 1998, the second Pratt Conference on "Future Petroleum Provinces" in 2000, and the first AAPG Conference on "A National Energy Policy" in 2000.

I have published scores of articles and two books, was selected twice as AAPG distinguished lecturer, and was honored by the Houston Geological Society as a "Living Legend in the Oil Business."

My proudest accomplishment was:

Being successively chosen as president of Pecten International, president of Arco International, and president of the American Association of Petroleum Geologists.

My biggest disappointment was:

I think I have learned more from my failures than from my successes. My largest failure was in the Gulf of Alaska frontier sale. Shell/Arco bid heavily on prospects, won the tracts, and found the tracts barren after drilling.

This was the first major sale in which I was in charge. I think I did a good job of assembling a team, focusing effort on key issues, and assuring that the technical and business effort was coordinated and completed by the sale date.

What did I do wrong? When I reviewed the work of the geophysicists, I found that they were very confident that subtleties in the data indicated an oil charge in the Gulf of Alaska reservoirs. My geophysical team gave me a written recommendation emphasizing their confidence about the oil charge to the prospects. I could not see the anomalies that they were confident really existed. I bowed to their judgment.

What did I learn? I learned that if I couldn't see an anomaly, if I couldn't understand a presentation, then that anomaly probably wasn't valid and that technical presentation probably wasn't correct. I learned that the company pays big bucks for my judgment, not the opinions of my staff. That's why the job of the senior manager can be a lonely one. The hard decisions are those when you must overrule your staff and have confidence in your own judgment.

I keep a framed seismic section from my Gulf of Alaska prospect hanging in my garage. Each time I enter my home, I am reminded of my imperfection and failures.

I learn from failure.

My advice to you is:

Make sure you love your job. Think what an advantage you will have over anyone else if your favorite reading material is from your chosen field. Think how blessed you will be if your time at work is personally rewarding and enjoyable. I have always remembered a horrifying quote — "The mass of men lead lives of quiet desperation." Don't be one of the masses.

Acknowledgments

I've been greatly helped along the way, and I hope I can thank my living mentors every day. In tribute to those who have passed on, perhaps I can encourage others to remember R. E. McAdams, Tom Hart, Barney Wilson, "Boo" Bernard, George Thompson, and Archie Hood.

William L. Fisher

Career history

1954	B.A. in geology, Southern Illinois University
1958	M.S. in geology, University of Kansas
1961	Ph.D. geology, University of Kansas
1986	D.Sc. (honorary), Southern Illinois University
2002	D.Eng. (honorary), Colorado School of Mines
	University of Texas, Austin, Barrow Chair and director, John A. and Katherine G. Jackson School of Geosciences

My proudest accomplishment was:

I think it was the opportunity to serve as president of AAPG. During my term (1985–1986), we experienced one of the worst falls in oil and gas prices in history. It was a traumatic time for many of our members, but I was impressed then, and continue to be, by the resiliency shown by my fellow petroleum geologists. I think the professional ties afforded by our geological societies go a long way in providing us this resiliency.

My biggest disappointment was:

There have been plenty, of course. But I try never to dwell on disappointments. I always like Willie Nelson's lines: "Remember the good times. They are fewer in number and easier to recall. Don't spend too much time on the bad times. Their staggering number will weigh heavy as lead on your mind."

Anecdotal story

Like oil and gas exploration, geologic research involves discovery, and that is the thrill of both. A meaningful discovery for me was the development of the concept of depositional systems. In the middle 1960s, I was doing a regional study of the Eocene Wilcox of Texas, generally considered a complex and not well understood stratigraphic unit.

I was not advancing as I liked until I had the fortune to hear two papers at the 1964 GCAGS meeting. One was by Jim Coleman and Woody Gagliano on the Mississippi Fort Jackson boring where they advanced the idea of bounding facies in deltas, and the other was by Don Boyd and Byron Dyer, who presented the then revolutionary idea that the South Texas Frio was a large barrier bar system. These two papers at one meeting really focused my thinking and with some further discussions with the likes of Dave Frazier and Rufe LeBlanc, it all came together.

My advice to you:

Don't be reluctant to expend energy. Use what intellect you may have to its fullest, keep disciplined — and you will accomplish much of what you want to.

Michael C. (Mike) Forrest

Consultant, Dallas, Texas

Career history
Born 1933

1955	B.S. degree in geophysical engineering, St. Louis University
1955–1992	Shell Oil Company
1992–1997	Maxus Energy Corporation
1997–2002	Consultant

My proudest accomplishments were:
From 1968 to 1975, I was part of the Shell Oil team that developed and applied "bright-spot" technology to discover more than 1 billion barrels oil and gas equivalent on the offshore Louisiana and Texas shelf.

From 1984 to 1987, I was in a leadership role on the Shell team that expanded Gulf of Mexico leasing and exploration, drilling out to 6000 feet of water. In the late 1980s, drilling discovered Auger, Mensa, and Mars fields. That was the beginning of a deep-water success story. Shell currently produces 500,000 BOE/day from the deep-water Gulf of Mexico.

My biggest disappointment was:
From 1981 to 1984, I was exploration manager with Shell in very high-cost exploration failures in Alaska frontier lease sales, including the Beaufort Sea and several basins in the Bering Sea.

An anecdotal story
In 1973, Shell drilled an exploration test on the west flank of a salt/share intrusive called Prospect Pine (Gulf of Mexico, SMI 130). Seismic data indicated four good amplitude anomalies ("bright spots"), but logs showed only three oil pays. Bill Scaife, our senior technology geophysicist, argued that he fourth "bright spot" should be a pay sand and the logs were wrong, whereas our petrophysicist stated that the logs were correct. A twin well was drilled 100 feet from the original hole to core the oil pay sands. Logs from this well showed a good oil pay associated with the fourth "bright spot."

Lessons:
- Seismic reflections are from an area (Fresnel zone), whereas well-log measurements are from a few inches to a few feet around the borehole (one interpretation of the above example is that the fourth sand is not present in a small area around the location of the original well).

- Both seismic and petrophysical measurements have inaccuracies that must be considered when making interpretations.

- Geoscientists must be persistent if they believe that a new idea or an interpretation is supported by good technical data.

My advice to you is:
- Strive for integrated technical studies.

- Continue to learn.

- Understand the risk analysis of projects that will be included in your company's exploration portfolio.

- Have fun in your work.

Joe B. Foster

Chairman, Newfield Exploration Company

Career history
Born Arp, Texas, 1934

1957	B.S. in petroleum engineering and B.B.A. in general business, Texas A&M University

Tenneco Oil Company

1957–1966	Petroleum engineer, Oklahoma City, Oklahoma, and Lafayette, Louisiana; handled bid economics for offshore lease sales
1966–1970	Headquarters staff; Houston, Texas; chief, economic planning and analysis
1970–1974	Vice president, exploration; leadership role in Gulf of Mexico sales
1974–1980	Senior vice president; president, exploration and production; headed worldwide exploration and production
1981–1988	Tenneco Inc., principal energy officer
1989–2000	Newfield Exploration Company, founder and chief executive officer
2000	Baker Hughes Inc., interim chief executive officer
2001–2002	Newfield Exploration Company, nonexecutive chairman

My proudest accomplishment was:
Founding Newfield Exploration Company in 1989 with $9 million of equity capital and leading it to become a publicly traded company with more than $2 billion of market value in less than 10 years.

My biggest disappointment was:
Seeing the company I had spent 31 years with, Tenneco Oil, be broken up and sold in pieces by its parent company in 1988. This was done to pay down debt incurred by another subsidiary — of all things, a maker of farm tractors! A true-value-adding organization was destroyed, and without its energy (and cash flow), the parent company withered away.

A story
The first three wells we drilled at Newfield were dry holes and one had a capsized rig, resulting in a $6 million loss which, if that well had not been turnkeyed, would have bankrupted Newfield. We had about $100,000 in the bank when we made our first discovery. New beginnings are fraught with danger.

My advice to you is:
- Focus your efforts in one or a few geologic provinces or geographic areas.
- Do your homework thoroughly, using superior technology.
- Always do what you say you are going to do.
- Be willing to take risks and obtain lots of exposure.
- Hedge against the downside.
- Live and work on the ragged edge between order and chaos.
- Remember that success and satisfaction almost always involve working cooperatively with other people.

L. W. Funkhouser

Career history
Born 1921

1943	A.B. degree in geology, Oberlin College
1948	M.S. degree in geology, Stanford University
1990	Doctor of science degree (honorary), Oberlin College
1948–1986	Chevron Corporation; final position, corporation director and vice president, exploration and production
1987–1988	President, AAPG
1991–2001	Chairman, AAPG Foundation

My proudest accomplishment was:
Being associated with the Chevron geologists and geophysicists who discovered major new petroleum provinces, such as the Overthrust Belt play in Wyoming, the Deep Tuscaloosa play in central Louisiana, the Hibernia Field offshore Newfoundland, the major oil discoveries in Sudan, and the West Pembina Devonian Reef in Alberta, among others.

My biggest disappointment was:
The dismantling of the highly talented exploration operations and research groups after the oil-price debacle of the mid-1980s.

Anecdotal story
In the early 1970s, Chevron and another company drilled a series of wildcats on the Grand Banks offshore Newfoundland. All were dry holes, but the last and most northeasterly test found an excellent source rock but no reservoir rocks.

Several years later, Chevron was offered a half interest in several million acres offshore eastern Newfoundland in exchange for a half interest in a 100,000-acre block in the Mackenzie Delta. Chevron's subsidiary, Chevron Canada Resources, under the leadership of G.G.L. Henderson, recommended approval because of the source section found in the earlier well. However, Chevron's executive committee emphatically turned down the trade because the Newfoundland acreage was located in "Iceberg Alley."

In the late 1970s, the company holding the offshore Newfoundland acreage had drilled some unsuccessful wells on the block and came back to Chevron with a proposal that Chevron would earn half interest in a 750,000-acre block in return for drilling one exploratory well.

Because of the excellent source section seen in the earlier Chevron dry hole, the proposed trade was again recommended to the Chevron executive committee. Because the company had a long-range commitment on a large semisubmersible and no ready place to use it at that time, the exploration project was approved, despite the fear of icebergs.

Chevron Canada reworked the seismic data shot by the acreage owner and proposed a wildcat location on a large fault-bounded anticline found on the reprocessed data. The well was drilled, and it discovered the Hibernia Field — a billion-barrel field and the first commercial production in a new petroleum province. Hibernia currently has by far the largest daily production of any Canadian field. If at first you don't succeed....

My advice to you is:
Stay current in the rapidly evolving usage of modern exploration technology. Stay flexible and abreast of geologic applications that can lead to employment opportunities in future economic times. Remember that the search for and discovery of new petroleum resources are still among the most fascinating and productive endeavors available to today's professionals.

Jim Gibbs

Career history
Born 1935

1957	B.S., University of Oklahoma
1959–1960	University of Texas
1962	M.S. in geology, University of Oklahoma
	President and chief executive officer, Five States

My proudest accomplishment was:
Seeing many of the young geologists that started to work in our offices as "professional apprentices" become successful geologists and independents.

My biggest disappointment was:
Finding out that so many geologists are better oil finders than I am.

My advice to you is:
Find a niche in the profession of geology that you really enjoy, and develop your career around it.

Robbie Rice Gries
Priority Oil & Gas Co. LLC, Denver, Colorado

Career history
Born September 14, 1943

1966	B.S. in geology, Colorado State University
1970	M.A. in geology, the University of Texas at Austin
1973	Instructor at Wichita State University and consultant, Texaco Inc.
1973–1977	Geologist, assistant district geologist, Texaco Inc.
1977–1980	Reserve Oil Inc.
1980–1992	Consulting geologist and independent
1992–present	President and chief executive officer, Priority Oil & Gas LLC

My proudest accomplishment was:
Getting my wildest idea (to date) drilled in south-central Colorado. Predicting Cretaceous and Jurassic rocks beneath the extensive San Juan Volcanic field, I used old reports from geologists in the 1950s. Subsequent work by the USGS had predicted that the volcanics instead would overlie directly the Precambrian basement — the accepted dogma in the early 1980s, when I started to develop this subvolcanic exploration project. Oil seeps in the area, which I had soused out, seemed to obviate the fact that there must be a Cretaceous section, but it was still a difficult concept to sell because of having to buck the dogma of the day.

When we drilled the first stratigraphic test and ran

out of rig before getting through the volcanics, it made the chase even harder. However, that well had more oil shows, which tested to be Cretaceous crude. When the first oil and gas test was drilled, 3450 feet of volcanics was penetrated before we drilled into Tertiary red beds. Another 2790 feet of Tertiary was penetrated before drilling into Cretaceous Lewis Shale and a typical San Juan Basin Cretaceous section.

The second dogma we had to overcome was that even if we found Cretaceous rocks, they would be totally overcooked because of the overlying and penetrating volcanics. The nearby San Juan Basin had an extremely high heat flow that put shallow Cretaceous rocks (2000 feet) into the dry gas window. What were our hopes for oil and wet gas at depths of 4000 to 9000 feet right in the volcanic field? Heresy!

Geochemical analysis after our drilling determined that our Cretaceous rocks were still in the oil window for most of the Sag basin at depths well below the San Juan Basin transition. The San Juan Basin was the thermal enigma, not the San Juan Sag!

An anecdotal story

On occasion when I have been "exploring," I have had a report or publication that "killed" the prospect. However, persistence and reasonable scientific skepticism sometimes overcame the negative. On two occasions, source-rock geochemistry pointed to "overcooked" rocks and poor potential. I collected new samples and had them run again, sometimes twice. In both areas, we found that the original study was erroneous and the two areas were not "overcooked" at all, but were in the oil or transition window.

On a couple of other occasions, when I was exploring beneath thrusted Precambrian, I had publications or reports that said the mountain flank was not thrusted, but was uplifted vertically. After promoting new seismic and additional drilling, we established that indeed these mountain fronts were thrust-bound and not vertical. And indeed, they were prospective beneath the edge of the thrust.

My biggest disappointment was:

My biggest disappointment has been in not getting my prospect and well drilled southeast of Jackson Hole, Wyoming. A gorgeous geologic setting — an anticline formed between the thin-skinned thrust belt and the foreland Gros Ventre Mountain thrust — it was at the apex of the Hoback (Greater Green River Basin) migration path for hydrocarbons. Although we had valid federal exploration leases, a court battle with antidrilling groups continued for more than 10 years and the prospect was never tested. This — after I had taken the antipetroleum parties on a field trip

and showed them the locations that had been drilled 25 years previously (they couldn't even see the locations because they had been returned to their original state so successfully).

My advice to you is:

Look where others have overlooked or thought something was condemned. Don't be afraid to buck the dogma. Don't be afraid to be wrong. And trust that you will continue to have new ideas — as long as you keep looking!

Robert D. Gunn

Independent, Wichita Falls, Texas

Career history
Born 1925

1949	B.A. degree in geology, University of Minnesota
1949–1953	The Texas Company (Texaco)
1953–1959	Consultant
1959–1975	Independent
1975–present	Gunn Oil Company

My proudest accomplishment
My proudest accomplishment was receiving the Sidney Powers Memorial award in 1997.

My biggest disappointment
My biggest disappointment was spending five years "in prison" (as chairman of the board for the Texas Department of Corrections), which required nearly all my time, because the prison system was in a phase of reform. During this five-year period, I was unable to stay up with advances in geologic technology, which haunts me to this day.

Anecdotal story
In 1961, the Palo Duro Basin of northwest Texas had no production. I had caused two dry holes to be drilled in Childress County, Texas, searching for production in a Pennsylvanian Canyon reef. The third well on this prospect proved impossible to sell. Therefore, sincerely believing in my work, I stubbornly began to drill the prospect myself, even though I would have to risk my all. Mr. O. P. Leonard of Fort Worth heard of my effort and responded by saying, "If that young character believes in the thing that much, I'll take the deal." We found the first production in the Palo Duro Basin, the Kirkland field.

This income sustained me through very difficult years for our industry. I had, in this period, been trying to lease the 6666 Ranch in King County, Texas. I finally succeeded in January 1969, with the stipulation that I put up $100,000 earnest money, to be relinquished if I did not sell the deal to a respectable company by August 1, 1969. I tried and tried but could not find partners. The terms were just too tough.

So, strongly believing in my theories and reasoning, I had bet everything I owned, and I was about to lose it. However, with the aid of a friend, Netum Steed, the deal finally sold on July 30, 1969, with only one day to go. The result was the discovery and production of about 150,000,000 barrels of oil.

The point I would like to convey is that if you totally believe in your work, beyond any possible rationalization, consider pursuing your efforts to the extreme — even to the extent of "risking the ranch." Rather than caution and good sense, the attribute that paid off for me was rational tenacity.

My advice:
Be tenacious.

Alfredo Eduardo Guzmán

Career history
Born 1947

1971   B.Sc., Texas Tech University

1973   M.Sc., Texas Tech University

Employer: Pemex Exploration and Production

My proudest accomplishment was:
To have reached the highest position an explorationist can achieve in Pemex, the Mexican oil company (Exploration V.P.), and in that position to be able to revitalize the exploration of the Tertiary siliciclastics that had pretty much been abandoned after the discovery of a supergiant Mesozoic oil province in the mid-1970s, and recently to be the first geoscientist to occupy an Operations V.P. for one of Pemex´s E&P regions (Northern).

My biggest disappointment was:
Not having my father — a petroleum geologist with Pemex for more than 35 years, who passed away in 1989 — to see my accomplishments.

Anecdotal story
My most appreciated anecdotes have to do with people saying that something couldn´t be done or that there were no hydrocarbons to be found in a given structure, play, or province where, with time, they were proven totally wrong.

My advice to you is:
To always look ahead, but never to forget to look back to what preceded us.

Michel T. Halbouty

My proudest accomplishments were:
- Being the first independent to explore and wildcat in Alaska, and discovering the West Fork Gas Field on the Kenai Peninsula in 1959, the first discovery by an independent in Alaska

- Being elected as president of AAPG

- Receiving the honorary degree of doctor of geoscience from the U.S.S.R. Academy of Sciences in 1990, and being named honorary professor at the University of Nanjing, People's Republic of China, in 1993

My biggest disappointment was:
I try to learn from my setbacks, not be disappointed by them.

My advice to you is:
Remember your heritage. Many great geoscientists have come before you, and they have much to teach you if you are willing to learn.

Frank W. Harrison Jr.

Consulting geologist and independent
Lafayette, Louisiana

Career history
Born Bastrop, Louisiana

1950	B.S. degree, petroleum geology, Louisiana State University
1950–1954	Union Producing Company; 1950, draftsman and geological scout in Jackson, Mississippi; 1950–1954, geologist in New Orleans, Louisiana
1954–1956	Seaboard Oil Co., geologist in New Orleans, Louisiana
1956–1957	Trans-Tex Drilling Co., district geologist in Lafayette, Louisiana
1957–1959	American Natural Gas Production Co., head geologist in Lafayette, Louisiana
1959–present	Independent and consulting geologist in Lafayette, Louisiana
1982–present	Optimistic Oil Co., president

My proudest accomplishments were:
All of the successful oil and gas wells that I have generated and participated in during my career.

My biggest disappointments were:
All of the dry holes that I have generated and participated in during my career.

An anecdotal story
When I was president of the AAPG in 1981–1982, the oil and gas industry was at its zenith of activity and prosperity. More than 4000 rigs were working in the United States. The AAPG membership was burgeoning, and the demand for geologists was unbelievable. Geologists were demanding salaries comparable to their weight in gold, and many received that compensation. It was the best of times, with oil prices projected to reach $100/barrel in five years. Naturally, the theme of my presidency was unbridled optimism. Upon my turning over the reins of the presidency, the executive committee gave me a sign as a joke. The sign in bold letters read "Optimistic Oil Company — Frank W. Harrison, President."

Upon returning to Lafayette, Louisiana, I began to think about that particular company name and its appropriateness for me. First, it totally reflected my attitude of how to explore for oil and gas (a pessimist never made it in this business), and second, Optimistic Oil Company was a name with great industry appeal. I incorporated the name, and Optimistic Oil Company was born in 1982.

My advice to you is:
Never give up. Be optimistic, and drill, drill, drill!

Roy M. Huffington

Chairman of the board, Roy M. Huffington, Inc.
Houston, Texas

Career history
Born 1917

1938	B.S. degree in geology, Southern Methodist University
1941	M.A. degree in geology, Harvard University
1942	Ph.D. degree in geology, Harvard University
1942–1945	Served in the U.S. Navy in World War II (18 months in the Pacific, 15 of which were in combat), ensign to lieutenant commander
1946–1956	Humble Oil & Refining Co., field geologist to division exploration geologist
1956–1990	Roy M. Huffington, Inc., founder and chairman, international petroleum operations
1990–1993	U.S. ambassador to Austria
1993–present	Roy M. Huffington, chairman; most time is spent in not-for-profit groups — educational, medical, charitable, cultural, and civic

Accomplishment
The discovery of major gas reserves (15TCF) in Kalimantan (Borneo) and the creation of the multibillion-dollar liquefied natural gas (LNG) business in Indonesia. Indonesia now sells LNG to Japan, Korea, Taiwan.

Disappointment
The fact that rampant corruption kept us from creating a major LNG business in Nigeria. This should be the richest country in Africa, and it is practically destitute.

Anecdoctal story
I went to Indonesia in January 1968, and in August 1968, I signed a production-sharing contract (PSC) with its national oil company, then known as Permina. At the time, Indonesia had a bad reputation in the oil industry. It had just overcome an attempted communist coup at the end of 1965 in which hundreds of thousands of people had been killed. The economy was in total shambles, with many people on the street. Shell Oil Company had just been nationalized, when I arrived with the stated objectives of looking for gas. No other company was interested in searching for gas at the time. What would you do with gas on an isolated island?

I knew that Japan had real problems with air pollution and that gas, as a clean-burning fuel, could help clean up the atmosphere. Indonesia was the closest source of potential gas supplies for Japan. I was convinced I could find adequate gas supplies, but the biggest problem would be the financing of an LNG plant and export terminal.

Politically, after two months of dealing with the Indonesians, I felt certain that the country would be stable for a good number of years. They were desperate for money to stabilize the country and were working day and night. The energy minister said that if they didn't do it this time, they may never have anything.

After the PSC was signed, it was difficult to bring in additional joint venturers. Some still were worried about the political side, some didn't like the terms of the LNG contract, and two rudely said that good deals never walk in the front door of an office. In spite of this, the right joint venturers were located and brought into the deal.

After part of our seismic exploratory work was completed, we located a large, deep-lying anticlinal structure about eight miles long and four miles wide. With some shallow oil and gas fields present in the deltaic sands of the East Kutai Basin, I was convinced that this was the first wildcat I had ever seen that was a certain producer. When drilled, it came in with 1200 feet of net pay, all gas except for a few shallow oil sands at the top.

A second location was staked two miles north of the discovery. It was only after considerable difficulty that it was possible to convince our joint venturers to agree to put up their share of the well costs. The discovery was gas. What could we do with it? I guess I had forgotten to tell them that the plan was to sell it to Japan.

When the second well came in with about 1100 feet of net pay, it was evident that we had a major discovery. When subsequent drilling proved as much as three trillion cubic feet of gas to that time, negotiations with the Japanese for a market of three million tons of LNG per year commenced. With the market arranged, the Japanese were then persuaded to finance two trains of an LNG plant for Indonesia.

Subsequently, the plant was expanded to eight trains and can now process four billion cubic feet of gas per day. It is currently the largest LNG plant in the world.

Advice
Never to give up, if you are absolutely convinced you are on the right project and the timing is correct. Find new and innovative ways to bring the project to fruition.

Harry Jamison

Career history
Born January 15, 1925

B.A. in geology, UCLA, 1949, with honors; attended Texas A&M and Oregon State in U.S. Navy program in World War II; postgraduate studies at UCLA; summer executive program, 1969, University of Southern California

1950–1966	Richfield Oil Corp., Bakersfield, California; Olympia, Washington; Los Angeles, California
1966–1985	Atlantic Richfield Co., Anchorage, Alaska; Dallas, Texas; Bellevue, Washington; Denver, Colorado,
1981–1985	President and senior vice president, ARCO Exploration Co.
1985–present	Consultant

My proudest accomplishment was:
For eight years, I led the team that explored the North Slope and found and began development of Prudhoe Bay. I am still proud today, some 40 years later, of that group of geologists, geophysicists, surveyors, engineers, construction foremen, drillers, tool pushers, landmen, and all the others who worked so well together in very difficult conditions and met with ultimate success.

My biggest disappointment was:
I saw the promise of Prudhoe Bay delayed by the politics of pipeline construction, and later the potential of ANWR delayed or prevented from even being evaluated, much less thoroughly explored or possibly developed.

Anecdotal story
A few years after the discovery of Prudhoe Bay, I was in a company meeting in Dallas (I was chief geologist at the time), and a review of finding and development costs was under way. One of the planners presented a chart which did not include Prudhoe as a component of reserves added. I asked why, and the response was, "That was an aberration. It skews the results and was just a lucky find." I admit I lost my cool and heatedly replied, "That makes me want to throw up! Ten years of hard work, plus a lot of vision and a lot of guts went into giving us the opportunity to get lucky." There was a period of silence, and then the meeting proceeded. The Prudhoe reserves were not included in the chart and were seldom included thereafter in similar calculations. Go figure!

My advice to you is:
Be persistent in nurturing your ideas and dreams and those of others. The easiest thing in the world to do is kill a new and "tender" idea (play). It takes strong, courageous people to provide the opportunity for new ideas to grow and develop to maturity.

James O. Lewis

Career history
Born 1922

1943	B.S.M.E., University of Kentucky
1949	M.S. in geology, University of Kentucky
1955–present	Consulting geologist

My proudest accomplishment was:
Several prospects which I caused to be drilled and found producing sands were based 90% on surface geologic interpretations, 10% on information from previously drilled wells, 0% on geophysical information.

My biggest disappointment was:
A prospect which was drilled in the same area as above did not produce, although numerous wells provided subsurface structural and stratigraphic control that was sufficient to justify some seismic expense, which confirmed the prospect. This was about 30 years after the above successes.

My advice to you is:
- Remember — not everyone you meet will have your best interest as the top priority.
- Be like the "Wise Old Owl" — learn to listen.
- There is no such thing as a free lunch.
- Enjoy what you do and you will do it well.
- Do what you enjoy, not what you have to.
- Be active in your professional society.

Tom Mairs

Career history
Born 1937, Newton, Kansas

1959	B.S. in geology, the University of Oklahoma
1962	M.S. in Geology, the University of Oklahoma
1961–1973	Humble Oil & Refining Company/Exxon
1973–1980	Alamo Petroleum Co., vice president of exploration
1980–1985	Carlson Petroleum Co., vice president of exploration
1985–present	Independent petroleum geologist

Proudest accomplishments
Being involved in the oil and gas industry with its unique camaraderie, and I am humbly proud to be included in this tribute to our truly legendary geologists and oil finders.

Biggest disappointment
Learning that the first exploratory prospect I had originated with Humble Oil & Refining Company during the early 1960s had been condemned for a future lakesite and would not be drilled. Other disappointments were the first and last dry holes that I caused to be drilled.

Anecdotal story

As district geologist in Humble's Talco District, I was successful, after many attempts by myself and several predecessors, in finally convincing management to drill a step-out well considerably downdip to the current water level in the giant Talco Field. It resulted in finding a stratigraphic trap containing several million barrels of additional oil — an excellent lesson in perseverance!

My advice to you is:

Be an unselfish and active contributor to our industry, to professional organizations, and to life. And if you are determined to be a true oil finder, like several of these legendary people, do nothing else, but seek and persevere!

Acknowledgments

To all of the many who have helped me through life, but especially to Helen Bradford, my high school English teacher, who taught me responsibility; to Jack W. Trantham and Stephen W. Schneider, whose superb exploration talents and wonderful senses of humor have been a long and continuing inspiration to me; and to Esso Production Research Company, for excellent training in petroleum geology.

John A. Masters

Direct Detection Experts, Denver, Colorado

Career history

I was born September 20, 1927, in Shenandoah, Iowa — in tall-corn country in the southwestern corner of the state. It was my father's town, with aunts, uncles, cousins, grandmother — a small, neighborly, bosomy place, still my dearest memory.

I grew up in Tulsa, Oklahoma, then the "Oil Capital of the World." Everyone we knew was in the oil business. My stepfather, John Bartram, was a leading geologist-executive in Stanolind, the precursor of Amoco.

Mother was a lovely woman, nearly an angel, but ever a firm counselor. My brother, Chuck, two years younger, tagged along for 15 years then — boom — got bigger and stronger, followed me to Yale, and became a geologist.

I went through school in Tulsa, grew up nearly, discovered sports, and discovered girls. I wasn't notably successful with the latter two categories. I was smart enough to skip the second grade but not smart enough or big enough to be a leader until I got to graduate school. I had to work full speed at school to keep up. What I learned there may not have been as important as learning that you have to stay at it — hard.

My last year in high school, 1944, I won a four-year scholarship to Yale at age 16. I had a modestly good record at Yale, but the competition was fierce. I tried to major in engineering, flopped, and settled on economics — boring. I took two courses in geology in my senior year and was hooked.

During graduate school at Colorado U., I took one year of undergrad courses, one year of grad courses, and spent one year doing research and writing my thesis. I was a good student with top grades and loved it all. I did fieldwork in summers for Amerada and loved that too.

I married in my last year of school and graduated in 1951. I went to work for the U.S. Atomic Energy Commission on the Navajo Reservation in northeastern Arizona, looking for uranium — except we were ordered to call it something else. Very spooky! Don't let anyone see your Geiger counter!

Susie was my wife, buddy, field partner, and later mother of three wonderful children — Chuck, Barbie, and Alan.

In 1953, I signed up with Kerr-McGee to be an oil geologist. I moved to Oklahoma City and was mentored by the great Dean McGee. I moved to Midland, in west Texas, in 1954 and studied Permian reefs. I moved to Denver in 1955, at age 28, as manager of uranium exploration and district geologist for oil and gas. I found Ambrosia Lake that first year by myself, in New Mexico, the largest uranium deposit ever discovered in the United States. I found it in a new formation, in a new area, in an entirely new geologic environment.

I didn't know it, but that element of novelty would become my trademark. Ambrosia Lake was a very important asset in the cold war. The Russians realized, to their horror, that we could make an unlimited number of atomic bombs. It was a new game.

In 1957, I was sent to Canada for more seasoning in oil. I returned to Oklahoma City in 1959 as regional exploration manager of half of Kerr-McGee's operations. The most important area we had was the Gulf of Mexico, so I spent a lot of time in New Orleans learning about Tertiary sands, growth faults, and salt domes. I got pretty good at it, but Mr. McGee was better, so I never felt very important.

I was appointed chief geologist in 1961, at age 34, probably the youngest chief geologist of a prominent company in the United States.

In 1967, I found Dineh-bi-keyah, Field of the People, on the Navajo Reservation, right in the uranium area I had worked so intensively. I did this by myself, with an idea that came to me alone on a Saturday afternoon in the Kerr-McGee office in Oklahoma City. I had left Arizona 14 years before and hadn't thought much about the area since then. But that Saturday afternoon, my subconscious mind finally put together a geologic picture it had probably been wrestling with for the whole 14 years. Suddenly, in a single flash, I saw all the data in my memory rearranged into a convincing regional structural picture. It formed a huge buried anticline 35 miles long under most of the uranium area I had worked so long ago. It was probably the largest undrilled anticline left in the United States. It was virtually invisible to anyone who had not walked and jeeped over nearly every mile of that structure. Indeed, it had stayed invisible to me for 14 years.

On that Monday, I went to Mr. McGee. He asked me about 20 serious, probing questions and then said, "OK." He was the clearest-thinking, most decisive man I've ever known. We drilled it and found no conventional reservoir rock, but it did have an igneous sill at 2800 feet — with good oil shows. Everyone wanted to plug it. McGee had sat a lot of wells as a young geologist for Phillips. This time, he didn't pay much attention to the rock type, the correlations, or the structural position. He was fixated on the oil show. He said, "Test it." No oil. He said, "Acidize it." No oil. Then he said, "Frac it." The well came in for 648 BOPD of 45° API gravity oil. We drilled 31 wells which produced an average of more than 500,000 barrels each from 2800 feet. Total production was nearly 20 million barrels.

That was my igneous intrusive field, mine and Mr. McGee's — a screwball, one of a kind. The rule learned from that was that you don't have to be entirely right — just right enough, and ahead of everyone else. And work for someone like Dean McGee.

My next assignment was as president of Kerr-McGee of Canada, in Calgary, starting in 1967. I stayed until 1973 and learned a lot, but made no discoveries. Mr. McGee decided I could be more useful in the Gulf and wanted me to transfer. I went to Oklahoma City and told my favorite person in the whole world that I didn't want to do that. I thought I had better opportunities in Canada. Mr. McGee wasn't upset. He looked at me with pride. "John," he said, "you can only keep a stallion in the corral for a short time. Eventually, he has to run free. Good luck. Let me know if I can ever help you."

It was shortly after this that Susie died. She took her own life in a terrible tragedy of loneliness and despair. I cannot recount it or explain it satisfactorily. I will not try again because it never works.

The next chapter was Canadian Hunter. Jim Gray and I left Kerr-McGee together and offered ourselves to every large company in Canada. We were not met with enthusiasm. Finally, Noranda Mines admitted that Jim was the son of one of its past directors. That carried a lot of weight in the old-style Canadian companies.

Pretty soon, we were hired to start up their entry into Canadian oil. The chairman was Alf Powis. He asked us how much money we would need. I said, "I don't see how we can spend more than $5 million a year." Three years later, our budget was $180 million!

I identified a very large area in western Alberta which I thought had an abundance of favorable leads to a new type of gas trap. It had never been described in academia or the literature of geology. No company accepted it as a meaningful exploration concept. I called it Deep Basin, to describe its position in the deep syncline (unfavorable), downdip from water (impossible), in low-permeability reservoirs (unfavorable), with lots of electric-log-calculated gas shows (undoubtedly a misinterpretation). This was not a propitious start.

On that first prospect, we drilled six dry holes, as described below in my anecdotal story. They cost $1 million each. Noranda was ready to jump ship. The seventh well hit big and discovered the largest gas field in the history of Canadian oil and gas exploration. Once again, you see, my exploration flashes favor the bypassed, unpopular regions.

At the same time, I found my wife Lenora. She cost about the same as Elmworth but is much more valuable. We have added two fine boys to our total family. Lenora is my greatest discovery.

The development of Elmworth and several other new fields followed apace. Our company grew from two to 325. We became the tenth-largest gas producer in Canada. We were famous — in Canada, at least.

In 1992, I was stunned to find that Noranda's corporate rules required all officers in the mother company and all subsidiaries to retire at age 65. I couldn't believe they wouldn't make an exception, but they wouldn't — something about visibility, bad precedent, and other bureaucratic crap. In 1994, I left Calgary after 27 years as a Canadian because I would not adapt to being a has-been in my industry, in my city, in my life. It was a cruel event, made more cruel by human selfishness and the opportunity which opened to those people for advancement.

A large independent in Denver named me president of his oil company and introduced me to his 20-person staff. I brought in two more ex-Canadian Hunters who are still the best technical people he has. I was there three years. He was used to people doing what he told them to do. I'm not very good at that. Nothing worked very well. He couldn't find oil and he wouldn't let me do it. Finally, he told me to leave. I had one day to pack up. I had been a successful geologist for 47 years. This was an interesting new experience.

I had one more job which was even more unsatisfactory, but again, a new experience.

Finally, I had to deal with the life lessons involved. I was counseled to be more cautious, more suspicious of people. At first, that made a lot of sense. But at last, I was unwilling to abandon my identity. I believed I had had a good career. Overall, I trusted and respected people and expected the same from them. The results, statistically, were quite good.

John Burns, president of Frontier Oil, called me for a talk. He explained his company, its purpose, its target. After an hour, he said he was trying to remake his company and wanted me to head exploration and my old, treasured friend Dick Wyman, from Hunter days,

to head engineering. I said instantly, "John, if you're smart enough to hire Dick Wyman, I'll join you." So much for a careful, cautious approach! But this time, my old way worked fine.

I stayed two years with Frontier, but our program in North Dakota failed, and the company disappeared.

Life in the U.S. oil business had not been very fulfilling, but I had a new idea. Frontier's reservoir engineer was a very smart fellow named Alan O'Hare. We were always able to deal with problems by combining our mental strengths rather than letting them create a contest. He is left-brained, analytical, and quantitative. I am right-brained, conceptual, and imaginative. Together, we get all the facts right and then paint in the blank spots to make a whole picture. It works fine if both partners are good enough.

We are now embarked on a whole new chapter. We formed DDX, Direct Detection Experts, L.L.C., to apply the well-evaluation lessons I had developed at Canadian Hunter. We find that the resulting measurements can exceed the more routine numbers ordinarily accepted by a busy industry focused on a particular set of problems in deep-water Gulf of Mexico and other marine environments. Amazingly, most of the onshore United States has been abandoned by the major companies because it is no longer favorable for finding large structures by seismic operations.

There are a few critical factors in reservoir evaluation which can be measured more accurately by precise microscope readings than by customary methods. It is also true that a few experts can read critical additional information from electric logs and drillstem tests. Careful attention should also be given to mud logs.

A small group of expert reservoir analysts under my direction changed exploration history in Canada. I think we can do the same thing in the United States. We have carefully analyzed enough dry holes in the United States to believe that there are literally thousands of bypassed wells that were incorrectly interpreted and subsequently abandoned. Elmworth was found in an abandoned area of 85 bypassed wells. We found Keg River Gething and Ring-Border the same way. We now have several very large, very promising bypassed prospects in the United States.

Over a long career, I have learned a vital lesson of exploration. It is rooted in science and engineering, but finally, it steps beyond them in wisdom and total experience. I have come to call it the Eleventh Commandment: *Thou shalt not give up.*

My proudest accomplishment was:
The discovery of Elmworth gas field in Alberta in 1976, the largest gas field in Canada.

My biggest disappointment was:
Retiring from Canadian Hunter at age 65.

Anecdotal story
Hanging in there by yourself is not easy. New ideas can be very unpopular.

I was young, and my small Canadian Hunter company had existed for only three years. Our parent company, Noranda, was a giant in the Canadian mining business and was very self-assured. My prospect at Elmworth in 1976 in Alberta was almost entirely countercurrent. It was bottom of the basin, downdip from water, an entirely new reservoir, and in the middle of a long trend of 85 dry holes. We drilled six dry holes costing $1 million each. My staff members were discouraged. They were sure the trend was northeasterly, but we had worn that out, and the Noranda board was rebellious.

I went to Toronto with maps to plead with the chairman for one more well. "Alf," I said, "this has to be a big field. There are just too many good indicators. We must be going in the wrong direction. Let's go northwest. Just one more well."

"John, one more million-dollar well might cost your job and mine too. The board thinks we're crazy."

I said, "We gotta do it. This could be a giant."

Long pause. Silence. "OK, John, it's just you and me. Make it good or we'll both be on the street."

We drilled it, had four Lower Cretaceous shoreline conglomerate zones at 6000 feet, tested them, and flowed a total of 24 MMCFD. Elmworth developed into the largest gas field in the history of Canada.

My company never did anything new that a majority agreed to. Majorities don't look down the road. They look in the mirror.

My advice to you is:
The United States still has large reserves of gas in low-permeability reservoirs in basin-center accumulations.

Acknowledgments
I have been blessed with very wise mentors who guided my way through the wide variety of experiences it takes to form a competent explorationist. Professor Warren Thompson forced me to think on a regional scale. Rodger Denison started me off as an oil geologist and gave me my first recognition. A. I. Levorsen was a friend and counselor. Mark Millard recognized me as a key executive in the great Noranda Company. Dean McGee taught me, guided me, and accepted me as a proven oil and gas and mineral finder. Mr. McGee was the grandest human being I have ever known.

Robert E. (Bob) Megill

Career history
Born November 26, 1923, Lawrence, Kansas

1941–1942	Carter Oil Co., Tulsa, Oklahoma
1942	Joined U.S. Navy (Seabees) in December; served three years
1944–1945	100 hours in naval officers' training, the University of Oklahoma
1945–1948	B.S. in geological engineering, the University of Tulsa
1948–1984	Carter Oil Co., Tulsa; transferred to Humble Oil, Houston (later known as Exxon USA); total of 40 years with the company
1984–1991	Petroleum consultant

My proudest accomplishments were:
The reception by peers of my writing, my books, and the monthly column for the AAPG *Explorer* which I wrote for almost 13 years.

The number of young people who thanked me for being their mentor.

The opportunities I had to teach within Exxon, AAPG, and the petroleum industry, in the areas of exploration economics, risk analysis, and personal productivity.

My biggest disappointment was:
The inability to convince the Offshore Division to accept an updated computer program for calculating bids for offshore leases.

My advice to you is:
Find out what you enjoy doing the most, and concentrate your skills in that area. Always consider part of your work to be training the young people who will follow you.

Charles G. (Gil) Mull

Petroleum geologist
Alaska Division of Oil and Gas, Anchorage, Alaska

Career history

Born 1935

1957	B.S., University of Colorado, Boulder
1960	M.S., University of Colorado, Boulder
1961–1965	Richfield Oil Corp., Anchorage, Alaska
1961–1962	Field geologic mapping and well-site geology, Gulf of Alaska district, Alaska Peninsula, and Yukon-Porcupine district, east-central Alaska
1963–1965	Field geologic mapping, Brooks Range and Arctic North Slope, Naval Petroleum Reserve #4 (NPR-4) and Arctic National Wildlife Refuge (ANWR)
1965–1967	Atlantic Richfield Company, Anchorage, Alaska
1965–1967	Field geologic mapping, Brooks Range and Arctic North Slope, NPR-4 and ANWR, and well-site geology
1967–1975	Exxon Co., USA, Los Angeles and Denver
1967–1973	Field geologic mapping, Brooks Range and Arctic North Slope; well-site geologist on Prudhoe Bay oil-field discovery and confirmation wells
1974–1975	Field geologic mapping, Chugach–St. Elias Mountains and Gulf of Alaska province
1975–1981	U.S. Geological Survey, Menlo Park, California, and Anchorage, Alaska, Office of National Petroleum Reserve in Alaska, and Branch of Alaskan Geology
1975–1981	Field geologic mapping, numerical modeling, and resource appraisal projects, National Petroleum Reserve in Alaska (NPRA), ANWR, and Arctic North Slope
1981–2001	Alaska Division of Geological and Geophysical Surveys, Fairbanks
1981–2002	Senior petroleum geologist, field geologic mapping, and resource appraisals, Brooks Range and Arctic North Slope, NPRA and ANWR; affiliate professor of geology, University of Alaska, Fairbanks
2001–present	Alaska Division of Oil and Gas, Anchorage, Alaska; senior petroleum geologist, field geologic mapping, and resource appraisals–basin analysis, Brooks Range and Arctic North Slope, NPRA

My proudest accomplishment was:

To have had the opportunity to be a member of a unique organization that fostered teamwork among a diverse group of geologists, geophysicists, landmen, engineers, construction foremen, tool pushers, and drillers, under a management that encouraged individual initiative, supported its people, and thereby successfully explored the North Slope and began development of Prudhoe Bay. It was the beginning of an outgoing career that has continued with the excitement of geologic discoveries in northern Alaska.

My biggest disappointment has been:

Politics and the extreme polarization of public opinion that have prevented further evaluation of the Arctic National Wildlife Refuge, which certainly can be done in an environmentally sound manner. Furthermore, it is a real shame that there has been so little progress toward a national energy policy that encourages responsible exploration and multiple-use development on public lands while simultaneously incorporating aspects of conservation and development of alternative energy supplies.

My advice to you is:

Be persistent in nurturing your ideas and dreams and those of others. The easiest thing in the world to do is kill new, innovative, and "tender" ideas or plays. It takes strong, courageous managers to have confidence in the abilities of their staff members to provide the opportunity for new ideas to grow and develop to maturity.

James F. Reilly II

So as Winston Churchill remarked years later about being turned out of office in 1946, "It was a blessing in disguise; and very well-disguised it was at the time!"

My advice to you is:
When I speak to schoolkids, I tell them that whatever they wish to do in life, the best thing to remember is that the only people who can tell them they can't do something and have it stick are themselves. Anyone else who tells them they can't do something can and should be proven wrong at every opportunity. This advice is good at any age, I think.

Career history
Born 1954

Education: University of Texas, Dallas, B.S., 1977; M.S., 1980

Employment: Enserch Exploration, Santa Fe Minerals, Dallas, Texas; National Aeronautics and Space Administration, Houston, Texas

My proudest accomplishment was:
I'm not really sure I've had it yet. I can look back at a lot of things that I'm really proud of — fields that I've worked on, places I've been, earning my Ph.D. while working full time, flying in space and not screwing anything up — but I think my best achievement is still being a dad to three teenagers.

My biggest disappointment was:
When I was in the aerospace engineering program at UT and on a USNR scholarship, I wanted to fly jets, go to test-pilot school, and shoot for an astronaut slot. Unfortunately for me, the end of the Vietnam War resulted in a huge reduction in personnel and the indication that I wouldn't get the chance to fly.

Big life-changing moment: I entered the geosciences program at UT–Dallas after spending a year and a half saving up some bucks to go back to school. That decision got me to the Antarctic, a really good job for 17 years in the exploration industry, and the opportunity to work on the seafloor and eventually to fly in space.

James D. Robertson

Career history
Born 1948

1970	B.S.E. degree in geological engineering, Princeton University
1975	Ph.D. degree in geophysics, University of Wisconsin
1975–2000	Atlantic Richfield Company (ARCO)
1975–1985	Geophysical and geological research
1985–1990	Domestic U.S. exploration
1990–2000	International exploration
2001–present	Rannoch Petroleum LLC
1994–1995	President, Society of Exploration Geophysicists (SEG)

My proudest accomplishment was:
Working constructively and creatively as an exploration executive with hundreds of ARCO people during 10 years of international exploration to find 1.5 BBOE net to ARCO (6 BBOE gross) of oil and gas reserves at a finding cost of less than $2 per boe. International petroleum exploration is a rich complexity of leading-edge science, major capital allocation, thoughtful risk taking, insightful strategic vision, wise portfolio management, global interpersonal relationships, and broad cultural diversity. Few other jobs offer such a rewarding and fascinating professional career, and I was privileged to work with a great group of people in ARCO's international exploration group.

My biggest disappointment was:
Not having enough good mentors during my career, and not realizing the importance of good mentors until late in my career.

An anecdotal story
In the early 1990s, I traveled to ARCO's office in Jakarta, Indonesia, with Marlan Downey, who at the time was ARCO's international exploration vice president. The Jakarta explorationists showed us their prospect inventory, including a carbonate feature that had been penetrated by some wells and had one or two high-rate tests. The exploration team waxed eloquent about the size of the trap and the strength of the charge. Marlan added to the enthusiasm by noting how much gas could flow through a single one-millimeter fracture intersecting a borehole, and then casually asked how much porosity would be present in a heavily fractured rock if one had only the fractures to hold gas.

The team shortly thereafter got the point — the feature was hopelessly uneconomic without connected matrix storage, despite the size and attractive flow-through fractures. The exchange was a memorable lesson that great oil and gas explorers quickly focus on the weakest elements of an exploration prospect. They carefully consider whether a weakness is a fatal flaw or instead an uncertainty that might be reduced through additional investigation. Time and effort are spent analyzing and quantifying weaknesses, not burnishing and extolling a prospect's obvious strengths.

My advice to you is:
Make lifelong learning a meaningful part of your professional life, recognizing that learning takes many forms, from on-the-job training to formal courses to volunteer activities to reading technical literature. Your job skills and your ability to work with others are the foundations of a successful career and make you valuable, independent of any particular employer. And don't hesitate to teach others or add to the technical literature yourself. That is when you find out what you really know.

Peter R. (Pete) Rose

Career history
Born 1935, Austin, Texas

1957	B.S. in geology, University of Texas, Austin
1959	M.A. in geology, University of Texas, Austin
1959–1966	Shell Oil Co., Houston, Miami, Corpus Christi, New Orleans
1968	Ph.D. in geology, University of Texas, Austin
1968–1969	State University of New York, Stony Brook
1969–1973	Shell Oil Co., Denver, Midland
1973–1976	Chief, Oil and Gas Branch, USGS, Denver
1976–1980	Chief geologist, Energy Reserves Group, Houston
1980–1998	Independent and consultant dba Telegraph Exploration, Inc., Telegraph and Austin
1988	Visiting distinguished professor, Kansas State University, Manhattan
1999–present	Managing partner and senior partner, Rose & Associates, LLP, Austin

My proudest accomplishments are:
Personal: Virginia, Cathy, Peggy (and Greg), Wally (and Kim), Jennifer (and Mark) — all living independent, educated, successful, and fulfilled lives; being married to Alice.

Professional: Through E&P Risk Analysis, I have helped more than 10,000 geoscientists and engineers learn how to evaluate their ventures objectively, making E&P more efficient, stockholders more prosperous, and prospectors more professional. I established Rose & Associates, LLP, in 1999.

AAPG: Through DPA and HOD, I have helped expand the influence of the membership in AAPG governance and improve AAPG business performance during 1995–2000, and I have helped expand mentoring and professionalism in AAPG.

My biggest disappointments were:
Personal: Taking 54 years to find Alice.

Professional: Not opening a big low-volume gas field in the Raton Basin in 1985, and nearly going broke in 1987.

AAPG: Contributing to the contentious AAPG atmosphere during 1997–2000, and bruising some friendships in the process. Change is painful.

Career reflections
I never had to worry much about getting motivated — almost every geological task I ever undertook fascinated, changed, and rewarded me, leaving indelible memories:

- balmy days on carbonate sandbanks in the Bahamas
- catching cores in the middle of the night in south Texas
- the creak of a lonely windmill on a summer evening after a day of mapping the Edwards Plateau
- tracing Carboniferous facies westward, range by range, across the Rockies
- despite USGS bureaucracy, building a relevant E&P research program and staffing it
- the bitter disappointment of every dry hole, and the jubilation of my few discoveries
- the fulfillment that came whenever I was able to serve a client well with sound, forthright, timely counsel
- finally learning to just tell it like it was, and simplifying everyone's lives in the process
- teaching risk analysis with Bob Megill and Ed Capen, and growing enormously in the process
- seeing sparks of insight kindle and grow in thousands of students
- building a thriving little company from a 20-year sole proprietorship
- learning what it took to become a professional, and deriving great satisfaction in trying to live like one
- 10,000 pleasant recollections of warm, lasting friendships in a global web of valued colleagues.

I've been accused of being a workaholic. Maybe so, but it was mostly fun to me and still is. What a blessing this lifelong geological career has been for me!

My advice to you is:
- Work hard at whatever gives you joy.
- Cast your bread on the waters.
- Live within your means.
- Tell it like it is.
- Give a damn.

Acknowledgments

Over the past 50 years, a lot of generous and gifted people provided special support, mentorship, and example (as well as some thoroughly warranted "swift kicks" as focused incentive). Among my geological mentors, I must acknowledge Charley Bell, Bob Folk, Baxter Adams, Ted Cook, Harry Thomsen, Jim Clement, Sid Bonner, Bob Megill, and Bill Fisher. Nongeological mentors include Floyd Davis, Edgell Pyles, Gerry Geistweidt, Charley Dowell, and Lynn Hughes. I am profoundly grateful for their friendship.

Jack W. Schanck

Career history

Born July 8, 1951, Pittsburgh, Pennsylvania

B.S. in geology, Allegheny College, Meadville, Pennsylvania

M.S. in engineering geology, University of Memphis, Memphis, Tennessee

1990–1992	President, Unocal Canada, Calgary, Alberta, Canada
1992–1994	Vice president, Worldwide Exploration (Unocal) Sugar Land, Texas
1994–1996	Group vice president, Oil & Gas Operations (Unocal), Sugar Land, Texas
1996–1999	President, Spirit Energy 76 (Unocal), Sugar Land, Texas
1999–present	Co-chief executive officer, Samson Investment Company, Tulsa, Oklahoma

My proudest accomplishments were:

There have been two — one personal and one professional. On the personal side, I was proud of raising a family and seeing them all become successful in their own rights.

On the professional side, my proudest accomplishment revolves around productivity of operations. While at Unocal, I led the turnaround of Unocal Canada from an operation that lost money to one that contributed 10% of the total worth of the company. While at Samson, in the last two years, I helped implement change that has led to an increase in value of about 50%.

My biggest disappointment was:

Not taking sufficient risk early in the pursuit of exploration opportunities, deep-water Gulf of Mexico, Unocal.

Anecdotal story

I had the opportunity to attend the initial Hedberg conference organized by Pete Rose on risking, held in Salt Lake City. It was, to my knowledge, the first time representatives from most major oil companies had met to discuss what we know and do not know about the subject of addressing risk in our business. The participation was all open, honest, involved, and concerned. I left the meeting with a strong appreciation for the importance of shared learning and of the high-caliber men and women who work in the industry.

After the conference, a few of us went horseback riding in the foothills. Forty-five minutes into the ride, I was thrown from my horse and landed in a patch of cactus — bringing me a whole new appreciation for risk assessment.

My advice to you is:

Seek out opportunities for change by looking at yourself first. Ask yourself, "How and what can I change that will have a positive impact on those around me?"

Harrison H. Schmitt

Career history

Born: Santa Rita, New Mexico, July 3, 1935; grew up in Silver City, New Mexico. Mother, Ethel Hagan Schmitt (educator and naturalist); father, Harrison A. Schmitt (mining geologist)

Education: Western High School, 1953; California Institute of Technology, B.S., 1957; Fulbright Fellow in Norway, 1957; Harvard University, Ph.D., 1964; NSF Postdoctoral Fellow, 1964

I have been privileged to acquire diverse experience as a geologist, pilot, astronaut, administrator, business-man, writer, and U. S. senator. My Ph.D. was based on geologic field studies in Norway. As a civilian, I received U.S. Air Force jet pilot wings in 1965 and U.S. Navy heli-copter wings in 1967.

I was selected for the NASA scientist-astronaut pro-gram in 1965. I organized the lunar science training for the Apollo astronauts, represented the crews during the development of hardware and procedures for lunar sur-face exploration, and oversaw the final preparation of the Apollo lunar module descent stage. I was designated as mission scientist in support of the Apollo 11 mission.

After training as backup lunar module pilot for Apollo 15, I served in that same capacity on Apollo 17 — the last Apollo mission to the moon. On December 11, 1972, I landed in the Valley of Taurus-Littrow as the only scientist and the last of 12 men to step onto the moon.

In 1975, after two years of managing NASA's Energy Program Office, I fulfilled a long-standing per-sonal commitment by entering politics in 1976. I served in the U.S. Senate from 1977 through 1982, represent-ing my home state of New Mexico. I was a member of the Senate Commerce, Banking, Appropriations, Intelligence, and Ethics Committees. In my last two years in the Senate, I was chairman of the Subcommittee on Science, Technology, and Space and of the Appropriations Subcommittee on Labor, Health and Human Services, and Education.

I later served on the President's Foreign Intelligence Advisory Board and the President's Commission on Ethics Law Reform, as cochairman of the International Observer Group for the 1992 Romanian elections, as vice chairman of the U.S. delegation to the 1992 World Administrative Radio Conference in Spain, and as chairman of the Technical Advisory Board for the U.S. Army Research Laboratory.

I consult, speak, and write on policy issues of the future, space, the science of the moon, and the American Southwest. I am chairman emeritus of the Annapolis Center (risk-assessment evaluation) and am an adjunct professor in the Department of Engineering, University of Wisconsin–Madison, teaching a course on resources from space.

My current corporate board memberships include Orbital Sciences Corporation and PhDx Systems, Inc., and I am a member of the Corporation of the Draper Laboratory. I am a founder and the chairman of Interlune-Intermars Initiative, Inc., advancing the pri-vate sector's acquisition of lunar resources and He-three fusion power and broad clinical use of medical isotopes produced by fusion-related processes.

I am honored to have received these awards: the 1973 Arthur S. Fleming Award, 1973 Distinguished Graduate of Caltech, 1973 Caltech Sherman Fairchild Scholar, NASA Distinguished Service Award, Fellow of the AIAA, honorary member of the Norwegian Geographical Society and Geological Association of Canada, 1989 Lovelace Award (space biomedicine), 1989 G. K. Gilbert Award (planetology), and Honorary Fellow of the Geological Society of America, American Institute of Mining, and Geological Society of London. I have received several honorary degrees from U.S. and Canadian universities.

My proudest accomplishment was:

It is hard to choose among surviving Caltech, complet-ing my Ph.D. at Harvard, becoming a jet and helicop-ter pilot, going to the moon, being elected to the U.S. Senate, being of some influence in lunar and planetary science, and persuading my wife, Teresa, to marry me.

My biggest disappointment was:

Probably none that is significant in retrospect, but not learning mathematics as a language comes close.

Anecdotal story

Sometime in late 1963 or early 1964, I remembered a most interesting visit with Gene Shoemaker in Menlo Park and decided to write him a letter to see if he was hiring geologists for his new USGS Branch of Astrogeology. Coincidentally, Gene had decided to contact the four geologists who had the top scores on the 1963 exam for Geological Survey employment to see if any were interested in joining his new branch, now headquartered in Flagstaff, Arizona. Gene's Astrogeology Studies Group, which I had visited in 1960, had morphed into a major new USGS initiative, largely funded by NASA contracts. Our letters of mutual inquiry literally crossed in the mail, and with the completion of my NSF Fellowship in June 1964, I headed back west.

Carolyn and Gene Shoemaker had decided in the spring of 1962 that Flagstaff would be a great place to live and raise a family, eventually persuading the leadership of the Geological Survey to locate the new branch there. Sadly, any reality of Gene realizing his dream of going to the moon had evaporated soon after our first meeting, in 1960. While working temporarily at NASA headquarters in Washington, he almost died from the effects of Addison's disease, a treatable but incurable thyroid deficiency.

As an unsuspecting and unsuspected surrogate for Gene in regard to his going to the moon, and with no comparable dreams, I arrived in "Flag" on July 7, 1964. At Gene's invitation, I began to look at the various projects under way as part of NASA contracts he had corralled.

Although I took a familiarization trip to the Caltech Jet Propulsion Laboratory where the lunar surveyor project was being managed for NASA, It was not clear to me exactly how I could contribute significantly to the effort. Gene's surveyor "television experiment" team was well staffed, led by geologist Elliot Morris and including photogrammetrist Ray Batson, geologist Hank Holt, and technology expert Jay Rennilson.

On the other hand, a more intriguing project, newly funded by NASA, needed someone as project chief. This was an effort to begin, for the first time anywhere, the definition of the types of observation, photographic, and sampling techniques that would be useful to the Apollo astronauts on the moon. What field geologist could pass up this challenge? Thus, I became chief of the Lunar Field Geological Methods Project, just before the arrival of several more geologists whom Gene Shoemaker had enticed to join him in Flagstaff.

With offices in the Arizona Bank Building in downtown Flagstaff, the Lunar Field Geological Methods Project picked up speed as Gordon Swann and I began to experiment with various possible field techniques that might be of use on the moon. Although both of us were total novices at looking at the various problems presented by this challenge, in retrospect, I now know that everyone else was also.

Certain things, however, were obvious as we began to think in the context of Apollo missions. Sampling of rock and soil and labeling the samples collected would be job one. The geologic context of those samples would be observation, verbal description, and photography of sample locations and other spatially and genetically related features.

Although many geochemists did not worry much about this context, geologists in general knew that without it, full and maybe correct understanding of much of the more subtle data obtained by analysis of the samples back on earth would be impossible. The challenge was to make these standard field geologic tasks as efficient as possible, given the operational constraints of a stiff, limited-visibility space suit, of radio communications as the only means of recording observations, and of all the other routine activities necessary to preserve life, limb, and mission. Little did we realize in those early days just how constraining these "operational" factors would become as actual Apollo exploration was planned years later.

In October 1964, years of discussion between the scientific community and NASA finally bore fruit — the National Academy of Sciences and NASA issued a joint request for applications from scientists and physicians for the first selection of scientist astronauts. The principal requirements were a Ph.D. or equivalent, born after July 31, 1930, six feet or less in height, and able to pass a rigorous flight physical.

It is hard for me to believe in retrospect, but I had not seriously thought about the possibility of becoming an astronaut until that announcement appeared on the office bulletin board. Reading it over, I thought for about 10 seconds and began to take steps to "raise my hand," that is, send in my application. I realized that I would regret not applying if humans actually went to the moon, and I might just have a chance to be one of them.

My advice to you is:

Prepare for as many unanticipated opportunities as possible.

John N. Seitz

Career history
Born 1951

1974	B.S. in geology, University of Pittsburgh
1975	M.S. geology, Rensselaer Polytechnic Institute
1977–present	Anadarko Petroleum Corp.

My proudest accomplishment was:
The discoveries made by my company (Anadarko) in Algeria, Alaska, the Gulf of Mexico, and East Texas (Berkine Basin, Alpine and Moose's Tooth, Mahogany, Tanzanite and Hickory, and Bossier Fields).

My biggest disappointment was:
My inability to convince my company to be an early deep-water player.

My advice to you is:
It is not enough to just have a good idea; you must be willing to submit that idea to public scrutiny.

Dan L. Smith

Career history
Born 1936

1958	B.S. degree in geology, University of Texas at Austin
1958–1967	Pan American Petroleum Corp. (changed name to Amoco; now BP Petroleum); transferred seven times in nine years
1967–1970	Roberts & Whitson Petroleum Corp., exploration manager
1970–1992	Texoil Company, part owner, executive vice president, and exploration manager
1992–1999	Meridian Resources Corporation, four years as a consulting explorationist; two years as vice president, exploration; one-and-a-half years as vice president, new ventures
1999–2001	Independent/consultant
2001–present	Sandalwood Oil & Gas, Inc., executive vice president, exploration

My proudest accomplishments
Career: Instrumental in drilling approximately 100 successful wells that led to the discovery of 30 new fields or major extensions.

Career: Developed an exploration program onshore Gulf Coast that included doing 3-D seismic before drilling, and demonstrated that 3-D seismic, although adding considerable capital dollars to the generation of a prospect, dramatically improved the economics of exploration. The company executing this program was the first independent to conduct 3-D seismic onshore.

This was during a time when 3-D was gaining momentum, but most people in the industry believed that the method would be uneconomic onshore.

Professional: Attaining the position of president of the American Association of Petroleum Geologists, an international organization.

My biggest disappointment

Career: Identifying and generating two large prospects which I was unable to lease. The first was the south half of a large onshore dome where the land was owned in fee by a major company. After trying to negotiate a farmout for at least five years, the fee owner drilled the prospect, resulting in the discovery of approximately one TCFG. The second was the west flank of an onshore Gulf Coast dome that was unleased when first checked. One month later, I sent land people to obtain leases, only to learn that a company had beat me to the punch by two weeks. That field ended up with 20 wells finding eight sands containing approximately 200 million barrels of oil.

Business: I had a major part in building a midsized independent company, Texoil, during the 1970s and early 1980s, only to have everything fall apart in the mid-1980s with the collapse of the oil and gas business.

An anecdotal story

The scene is the late 1980s, and once again, my world seems to be collapsing. The oil and gas business has been declining for seven years, and it is evident that the company in which I am a partner will not survive. I have three children in college and a fourth primed to enter college soon. I try not to panic. What to do?

New technology, 3-D seismic, had been working successfully in reducing exploration risk offshore. My expertise was onshore, where I had an inventory of prospects based on 2-D seismic. I put together a plan to find a company willing to risk using this new technology onshore. It worked. I was able to stay in business as an explorationist and get my children through college.

Again, I learned a valuable lesson: In the middle of difficulty, there is always opportunity.

My advice to you is:

The oil and gas exploration business is cyclical, with serious downswings and upswings. The successful explorationist should be prepared to change jobs — and possibly careers — several times in a lifetime. However, although it might seem bleak, this situation exists in nearly every industry in today's technological world. A career in geoscience offers the unusual opportunity of a lifetime in a very satisfying professional career. The following three things are critical:

- Professionalism and ethics are first and foremost. The reputation that one establishes will determine success. One screwup in ethics can ruin a career.

- Continuing education is necessary to stay current with fast-changing technology. Half of what one uses in technology will be out of date in approximately five years.

- Contacts and business relationships are essential. Thus, actively volunteering in local and national professional societies, where most contacts are made, is a big plus.

Acknowledgments

I find it very difficult to name specific individuals who have influenced my professional life. There are simply way too many to list. Instead, I will state that my affiliation and support of local and national professional societies are the factors that have allowed me to have an active and fruitful career as a petroleum explorationist. The hundreds of friends and associates I have known through these activities continue to make a difference in my career and personal life.

Robert M. Sneider

Sneider Exploration, Inc., Houston, Texas

Career history

Born 1929

1951	B.S. degree in geology (three years in engineering), Rutgers University
1951–1952	U.S. Army Corps of Engineer officer, U.S.A. and Korea
1962	Ph.D. degree in economic geology and mining engineering, University of Wisconsin, Madison
1957–1974	Shell Oil and Shell Development Companies
1974–1981	Sneider and Meckel Associates, Inc., an exploration and geoscience–petroleum engineering consulting company
1981–present	Robert M. Sneider Exploration, Inc., an exploration, property acquisition, and development geoscience–engineering consulting company
2000	Elected to the National Academy of Engineering
2001	AAPG Sidney Powers medalist

My proudest accomplishments were:

- Building or helping to build five financially successful small companies, including Sneider and Meckel Associates, Greenhill Petroleum, and Canadian Hunter Exploration.

- Sharing my views on E&P, petrophysics, and teams to thousands of geologists, geophysicists, petrophysicists, petroleum engineers, and managers through the AAPG, SPE, SEG, and different training organizations.

- Finding new hydrocarbon reservoirs in economically marginal fields and in new wild cats.

My biggest disappointment was:

Drilling unsuccessful wells or failed recompletions.

My advice to you is:

Learn the fundamentals of petroleum accumulation and production, including physical-chemical properties of rocks and fluids.

Acknowledgments

Many colleagues and coworkers have had a significant impact on my professional career and have helped me to achieve what success I have had. Three people, however, have had the greatest impact — Dr. B.F. Leonard, Dr. John J. Prucha, and Mr. Gus Archie.

In the 1940s, Leonard was a U.S. Geological Survey geologist at Princeton University and Prucha was a professor at Rutgers University and later a New York Geological Survey geologist. Both Leonard and Prucha were excellent teachers who exhibited a passion for geology that was infectious. They also taught me the value of detailed structural and stratigraphic mapping and the importance of understanding rock petrology in regional exploration. They were my models for how dedicated earth scientists apply theory to the search for mineral wealth.

Gus Archie, a research manager at Shell Development Company, hired me in 1956 and guided my early career in development geology and petrophysics at Shell. Archie was a quiet, unassuming genius but a superb teacher and mentor. He taught me how to view subsurface fluids and rocks on both exploration and development scales.

Discoveries and property acquisition that I have been associated with are the result of philosophy and knowledge gained from the association with Archie, Leonard, and Prucha, as well as many other colleagues.

H. Leighton Steward

Career history

Born 1934, Fairfield, Texas

B.S. and M.S., geology, Southern Methodist University

1962–1979	Shell Oil Company, division exploration manager and chief exploration operations, worldwide
1979–1981	Burlington Northern, vice president energy and minerals
1982–1997	Louisiana Land & Exploration Company, chairman, president, and chief executive officer
1979–2000	Burlington Resources, vice chairman

Former chairman of the U.S. Oil & Gas Association, Natural Gas Supply Association, National Wetlands Coalition, and All-American Wildcatters

My proudest accomplishments were:

- Working at Shell with Mike Forrest to document "bright spots" (about two years ahead of the industry) and then leading offshore GOM lease sales that used that information to dominate the sales in the early and mid-1970s.

- Successfully founding, organizing, hosting, and facilitating annual meetings of all the key energy industry association's leadership (the paid presidents and the current company chairmen) to forge unified messages to state and national governments — API, USOGA, IPAA, NGSA, NOIA, DPC, and NPRA.

My biggest disappointment was:

Not being successful at selling the idea of a unified, relatively inexpensive way to improve our industry's public image. We are still lying on the floor and letting people and the media kick us in the ribs with false and very misleading statements. We make only faint and belated efforts to set the record straight and educate the public about our industry's true value to people of the U.S.A.

My advice to you is:

Work hard, play hard. In my observations in several companies during many decades, the most creative people were the ones who were always "turned on" — whether at the office or at gatherings outside the office.

M. Ray Thomasson

Career history

1959   Ph.D. in geology, University of Wisconsin (B.S. and M.S., University of Missouri)

1959–1976   Shell Oil Company, where I worked as both a geologist and a geophysicist. Positions during that time included manager of geologic research; manager of the Texas, Louisiana, and Atlantic offshore division; manager of forecasting, planning, and economics; and head of strategic planning for Shell International Petroleum Corporation, London, England. My last position with Shell was as chief geologist for Shell Oil U.S.A.

1976–1990   Various positions, including vice president of exploration for McCormick Oil and Gas, Inc.; president of Spectrum Oil and Gas, Inc.; president of Pend Oreille Oil and Gas, Inc.

1990–present   Thomasson Partner Associates, Inc. (founder)

Board of trustees and past chairman of the board of trustees of the American Geological Institute Foundation

President of the American Geological Institute

1987–1988   Distinguished lecturer on stratigraphic geophysics in carbonates for the American Association of Petroleum Geologists

1995   Distinguished Service Award, AAPG

2003   Honorary member, AAPG

Past president of AAPG

Distinguished Alumnae Award, University of Missouri

Distinguished Alumnae Award, Geology and Geophysics Department, University of Wisconsin

My proudest accomplishments

After 43 years in the exploration game, it is difficult to pick one major accomplishment. I am most proud of having been fired twice from jobs as president of companies and not letting it slow down my career. This past 13 years of building Thomasson Partner Associates into a superb exploration organization with an outstanding staff and an outstanding track record has been both a significant challenge and a great pleasure.

My biggest disappointment

Each dry hole seems worse then the last one.

Anecdotal story

I was having lunch with my Shell mentor Mr. R. E. (Mac) Adams, who was 84. He had retired from Shell at 60, had successfully started and sold two previous companies, and had just started his third company. All of a sudden, he hit the table with his fist and said, "Damn, Ray, I wish I had 20 more years" — but not to do the things retired people do. He wanted 20 more years to explore for oil and gas. That is how I feel.

My advice

Never give up. Because of the ups and downs of our business, it is easy to lose faith that it is really worth the effort. Success, however you decide to measure it, is worth great effort. However, you must make it a wonderful ride, because the journey is more important than the destination.

Jack C. Threet

Threet Energy Inc., Houston, Texas

Career history

1928	Born in Dundas, Illinois
1951	B.A. in geology, University of Illinois
1951–1987	Shell Oil Co.
	I started work in Tulsa, Oklahoma, as junior stratigrapher and rose to vice president and head of exploration, from 1978 until my retirement, in 1987. I worked on technical and managerial assignments in numerous cities across the United States and in Holland, Australia, and Canada.
1953–1955	U.S. Army, Korea

My proudest accomplishments were:

As a young geologist (aged 28) at Shell, I single-handedly found South Autwine Field (~5 MMBOe) in Kay County, Oklahoma, a stratigraphic trap in lenticular Pennsylvanian sands, with subsurface geology (no seismic).

As vice president of Shell Oil Company's international ventures in 1974–1978, I led our small staff of exploration geologists and geophysicists into select new exploration ventures with early major success (several hundred million barrels each) in countries such as Cameroon, Syria, and Sabah (Malaysia). These discoveries materially added to Shell Oil's production and reserve base.

As corporate head of exploration for Shell in 1978–1987, I led a staff of as many as 600 geologists and geophysicists into exploration opportunities both at home and abroad. I am especially proud of having headed a team that led Shell into the Gulf of Mexico

deep water. There, as "true pioneers," we acquired an early, dominant acreage position and led industry for many years in discoveries and production of oil and gas, particularly in ultradeep water.

At the time we plunged, there was considerable uncertainty that even with exquisite geophysics and geology, commercial quantities of hydrocarbons could be found. In fact, Shell's discoveries proved huge and profitable and have had a major impact on the company's production levels, reserves, and earnings.

My biggest disappointment was:

I was general manager of E&P for Shell Australia in 1970–1972 when, as a partner in a joint venture, we drilled the discovery well at Rankin Bank, a huge structure in shallow water on the Northwest Shelf of Australia. In less than a week, our excitement turned to disappointment when the thick hydrocarbon-bearing sands we saw in drill cuttings and cores from the well were confirmed to be gas/condensate pays, not oil pays. As an oil field, Rankin Bank would have been one of the world's largest, and immediately profitable. As a gas field, although still large by international standards, Rankin Bank would take more than 20 years to prove its economic value.

An anecdotal story

My experience in business and in life generally may well be an example of how one should never underestimate one's ability, regardless of circumstances. One such example follows:

I remember vividly that hot June day in 1951 when I arrived in Tulsa by coach on an overnight train from Saint Louis to report to Shell, for $300 per month. Inexperienced, broke, and alone (my wife had stayed in Illinois to work), I walked, suitcase in hand, from the train station to Shell's office. I reported to area exploration manager R. E. McAdams, recognized by many as Shell's toughest taskmaster. Somehow, I managed to get through that session with "Mac." From that day on, I knew that no assignment or problem could ever present a larger gap between the task at hand and my perceived ability to deal with it successfully — a philosophy which served me well during those 36 years at Shell and is still doing so.

My advice to you is:

While in school, get a solid education in the basics of geology, geophysics, and petroleum engineering. With such knowledge, you will rightly develop a "can-do" attitude. After graduation, join an E&P company, small or large, but make sure it is a company that does not just pay lip service to the technology you can bring to bear. Instead, make sure as much as you can that it is a company that will recognize and consistently apply your expertise in making exploration investment decisions.

After experience and success with that company, you can elect to stay and rise to higher levels of responsibility or to go out on your own, confident that in either case, you will succeed.

Acknowledgments

In Shell Oil Co., I had dozens of mentors, including many well-known personalities such as R. E. McAdams, head of Shell's Exploration Department for much of my career and to whom I obviously owe a lot in the advancement and success of my career. John Bookout would certainly be another mentor, without question. However, I truly believe the most valuable yet least well known of all my mentors was my very first one at Shell — J. Rex McGehee.

When I joined Shell in Tulsa as a junior stratigrapher, inexperienced and fresh from the University of Illinois, Rex was area stratigrapher. A seasoned pro, he immediately took me under his wing and patiently taught me, one-on-one, how to "run" drill cuttings under the microscope. More important, he convinced me that although making accurate sample logs was apparently mundane, it was extremely important and valuable. "So always do your very best to do it right," he said.

That job I did for my first two years at Shell was part of a team effort to build formation correlation sections across the then very lightly explored Williston Basin. I know for a fact that many of my sample logs remained in Shell files and were regularly used by Shell geologists for at least 30 years.

Gene Van Dyke

President, Vanco Energy Company

Career history
Born November 5, 1926

1947	Mud engineer during college on Kerr-McGee's Ship Shoal Field offshore Louisiana, industry's first oil discovery out of sight of land
1950	B.Sc. in geological engineering, University of Oklahoma
1950	Geologist, Kerr-McGee Corp., Oklahoma City, Oklahoma
1951	Geologist, S. D. Johnson, Wichita Falls, Texas
1952	Independent producer and operator, Wichita Falls, north- and west-central Texas
1958	Van Dyke & Mejlaender, Houston, exploring and developing oil and gas fields of the upper Texas Gulf Coast and southern Louisiana
1962	Formed Van Dyke Oil Company, active in southern Louisiana
1967	West Lake Arthur, Louisiana, discovery; reserves 2+ TCF.
1973	Company's activity shifts to North Sea; purchases 25% interest in Tenneco's licenses offshore Netherlands
1982	Rijn discovery (P/ 15), 40 MMBO reserves, later 400 BCF discovered
1983	P/9 discovery, later named Horizon Field

1997	Awarded the Anton & Astrid Marin permits offshore Gabon, beginning Vanco's era of deep-water exploration offshore Africa
2001	Vanco Gabon Group drills offshore Gabon in world-record water depth of 2791 m
2002	Active offshore African countries, with more than 20 million net acres under license

My proudest accomplishment was:

In the last several years, I have led my company into deep-water West Africa, where we have become the largest license holder, with more than 26 million acres. We have acquired 2-D and 3-D seismic and have found more than 50 major structures.

My biggest disappointment was:

Our last dry hole.

My advice to you is:

Educate and train geologists and geophysicists as explorationists who emphasize exploration in deep water, because this is where the remaining significant reserves are to be found.

J. C. (Rusty) Walter III

Career history
Born 1957

1980	Degree in geology from the University of Texas at Austin
1982	Master's degree in business administration from the University of Texas at Austin
1982	Joined father to form Walter Oil & Gas Corporation, serving as vice president
1988–present	Chairman and CEO, Walter Oil & Gas Corporation

My biggest business accomplishment

My biggest business accomplishment to date has been my involvement in the discovery and operation of the South Marsh Island 36/37 (1989) field and the West Delta 106/107 (1993) field. Combined production from these two fields to date is more than 211 bcf of gas and nearly 19 million bbls of oil. We continue to operate these two fields, which produced approximately 50 mmcf/day and 3000 bbls of oil from about 12 wells (2001).

My biggest disappointment

My biggest disappointment would have to be the gas-price crash in February 1992, when gas fell below $1.00 per mmcf. We had to put several properties up for sale to pay down debts in a terrible market for sellers. Fortunately, the price rebounded in the fall, and we canceled the sale as gas reached $2.50 per mmcf!

My advice is:

Do not follow the crowd. The oil and gas business is extremely cyclical, and there is no better competitive advantage than to make sure your financial situation lets you play this volatility to your advantage. Having money when prices are low means you get your pick of the best prospects, leases, deals, etc., and during this time, drilling costs are at their lowest. We always strive to expand our business when things seem their worst.

Robert J. (Bob) Weimer

Career history

Born September 4, 1926, Glendo, Wyoming

1944–1946	U. S. Navy
1948	Married Ruth Carol Adams; four sons, Tom, Loren (deceased), Paul, Carl
1948	B.A., University of Wyoming
1949	M.A., University of Wyoming
1953	Ph.D., Stanford University
1949–1953	Union Oil of California, Rocky Mountains, Canada, west Texas
1953–1957	Consulting geologist, petroleum exploration for stratigraphic traps
1957–present	Colorado School of Mines
1965–1970	Department head
1958–1983	Getty Professor
1983–present	Professor emeritus
1961	Visiting professor, University of Colorado
1967	Fulbright lecturer, Adelaide University, Australia
1970	Fulbright lecturer, University of Calgary
1975	ITB, Bandung, Indonesia

AAPG president and Sidney Powers Medal, 1991; Distinguished Educator Award, 1996

SEPM president, 1972; Twenhofel Medal, 1995

AIPG Parker Medal, 1986

Member, National Academy of Engineering, 1992

ISEM Hedberg Award, 2001

Honorary member, Nigerian Mining and Geoscience Society, 1992

Honorary member, Canadian Society Petroleum Geologists, 2002

My proudest accomplishments were:

Personal: Marrying Ruth and watching the growth and successful careers of our family; educating full-time students at the Colorado School of Mines and other universities; offering on- and off-campus short courses for 25 years to more than 2500 people from more than 40 companies (the course: stratigraphic principles and practices in petroleum exploration and production).

AAPG: Assisting Dan Busch in starting and lecturing in the Continuing Education Program; being president of AAPG and of SEPM; helping to plan and implement the Division of Environmental Geosciences; being selected twice as an AAPG Distinguished Lecturer and as the first Huffington lecturer to southeast Asia.

Professional: Discovery of stratigraphic-trapped oil and gas in Green River and Powder River Basins, Wyoming, in the 1950s and 1960s.

My biggest disappointments were:

After the above discoveries, recommending prospects in the 1980s and 1990s that were dry holes.

An anecdotal story

The following summary is a story about oil and gas discoveries that have four components: an informal partnership to finance regional stratigraphic studies to find drillable prospects; a creative geologic model for petroleum fields in stratigraphic traps in Cretaceous rocks; a company willing to take a high-risk exploration program; and a high standard of ethics that acknowledged and protected the creative efforts of individuals and companies.

New pipelines and successful deep drilling to the Mesaverde Group on anticlinal structures created a high interest in gas exploration in the 1950s on the western margin of the Washakie Basin and the Wamsutter Arch. Mesaverde production was established on closed anticlines at Sugar Loaf (1953), Canyon Creek (1954), and Table Rock (1954).

Most companies initially prospected in these areas using conventional structural leads (i.e., closed anticlines or faulted noses). In 1954, however, Chester Cassel and I applied stratigraphic-trap concepts to these areas and other Rocky Mountain basins. Our approach integrated subsurface data with outcrop work and used an exploration model of predicting linear shorelines in areas where hydrocarbon entrapment could occur without structural closure. This model was developed from Cassel's two-year study of Mesaverde gas production at the giant Blanco Field in the San Juan Basin, and from studies of shoreline sandstones by API Project 51 along the Gulf of Mexico.

By early 1956, I had developed a play north and west of Table Rock Field, based on projection of shoreline trends across Wamsutter Arch. Exploration targets were the productive transgressive shoreline sandstones of the Almond Formation (upper Mesaverde, Table Rock Field) and the regressive shoreline sandstones of the Fox Hills Formation. Forest Oil Company, through recommendations of Don Lawson, George Veronda, and Jim Barlow, purchased the prospect and available lands during the summer of 1956. Forest later formed the Arch Unit (21,514 acres) and then drilled gas and oil discoveries. Producing acreage on the Arch Unit later became the north half of the Patrick Draw and the southern third of the Desert Springs Field.

Two surprises came out of the drilling — first, the large oil occurrence at Patrick Draw in what previously had been regarded as a gas-prone area, and the large area of stratigraphic-trapped oil and gas, an anomaly in the region, which was known for small accumulations on anticlinal closures.

The stratigraphic concepts related to shoreline trends, proved by field development in the 1950s, are still used as analogs for exploration and development programs in the deeper portions of the Wyoming basins.

More details about "selecting the prospect area, selling the deal, and unitization, drilling, and discovery" are presented in the paper "Stratigraphic plays of the 1950s on the Wamsutter Arch: Wyoming Geological Survey Guidebook — Resources in Southwestern Wyoming," 1995, p. 1–11.

The above-described prospecting work was followed by exploration in the Powder River Basin in the 1960s that led to discovery of the Manning Ranch Field, and royalty interests in the Spearhead Ranch and Powell Units.

My advice to you is:

Since retiring from full-time teaching at CSM, I have continued to do consulting work and prospect generation. I follow the advice that I pass on below.

- Never stop dreaming.
- Never stop doing.
- Never stop thinking.
- Never stop learning.
- Never stop being grateful to those who paved the way.

Acknowledgments

In a free society, opportunity and the avenue for success in a chosen professional career are provided by the continuity of universities, corporations, and governments. As institutions, they continually encourage education, application, and transfer of knowledge, and especially participation by youth — the next generation. This happened to me.

Opportunity started with service in the U. S. Navy during World War II, followed by earning geology degrees at the University of Wyoming and Stanford University. At Wyoming, I was guided and influenced by Professors Don Blackstone, Sam Knight, and Bill Thomas, and at Stanford by Sy Muller, a protégé of Hugh Schenck, and Fred Humphrey.

My professional career in industry grew by the direction and friendship of Horace Goodell and Dan Merriam, in consulting work from Chet Cassel and Paul Pustmueller, and in academics at the Colorado School of Mines, from John Haun, L. W. LeRoy and T. H. Kuhn.

And last, the greatest contribution to my success has been Ruth and our sons.

To all of the above and to many unnamed friends and former students, I acknowledge your support and extend my deepest gratitude.

Cindy Yeilding

BP America, Inc., Houston, Texas

Career history

1960	Born in Dallas, Texas
1982	B.S. in geology from Southern Methodist University, minors in art history and anthropology
1984	M.S. in geology from University of North Carolina
1985–1994	BP, Houston, Texas; exploration, operations, development and production geologist Hired as a carbonate specialist, then worked well-site operations for 1.5 years (longest continuous stint one month offshore). Moved to offshore development/production, where I planned development wells and recompletion programs and (the most fun of all) worked as Amberjack (MC 109) sanction geologist. More well-site work. Gulf of Mexico exploration from 1989.
1995–2001	BP, Houston, Texas; subsurface team leader, deep-water Gulf of Mexico, Venezuela Exploration and Geophysical R&D Team leader for several Gulf of Mexico Exploration Teams, a joint BP/Amoco Venezuela exploration team, and a seismic R&D team. Focus on acreage acquisition, regional studies, new play analysis, prospect generation, and drilling. Tested five deep-water prospects. Team led on three discoveries (Thunder Horse, Thunder Horse North, and Blind Faith) and had two failures.

Member of two technology-award-winning teams — one for breakthroughs in 3-D seismic depth imaging and one for drilling advances in the deep-water Gulf of Mexico.

2001–present	BP, Houston, Texas; global geoscience technology manager, Upstream Technology Group (technology unit leader)

My current job is to create opportunities for the R&D geoscience team to deliver significant business value for BP. The main roles include setting vision and strategy for geoscience technologies, providing links to the business, and promoting and evolving the role of UTG and new technologies across our company. Another key aspect of my job is to steward geoscience R&D projects and technical networks.

My proudest accomplishments are:

Professional: Being part of a team which conceived of and successfully tested a new play.

Personal: Tyler Anne Yeilding Donovan, born February 3, 2001.

My biggest disappointment was:

Becoming complacent, by simplifying geology.

My favorite story

There are so many ... but my favorite learning experience was when I worked on Mississippi Canyon 109 (Amberjack, Gulf of Mexico) as the sanction geologist. We had a wonderful small integrated subsurface team (Wayne Wilson as geophysicist, Tom Morrow as reservoir engineer, and me as geologist) working on the big decision: Do we develop this discovery or not? The project was described as "break even" at best. Our partners even gave us their 50% interest in the block after five penetrations — they just couldn't see how we could turn a robust profit.

We had a wonderful subsurface story — a strong geologic model (which still holds up today), an excellent data set, and multiple models and risk scenarios for development planning. It was some of the most exciting geologic work I've ever been a part of, but no matter what we did, the economics were dangerously "break even."

Meanwhile, the facilities engineers were busy planning for a tension-leg platform, because conventional wisdom dictated such a platform as the facility required to develop petroleum in 1000'+ water depth. We were still struggling to find a way to assure profitability. Then a relatively inexperienced engineer (Thyl Kint) asked a simple question: "Why not a conventional platform — just in deeper water than we've done before?"

Well, his idea worked. The platform was designed and built, expanding on proven techniques — at a significantly reduced cost of development and significantly improved economics. Suddenly our little baby was robustly economic, all thanks to a surface guy thinking "outside the box." He was immediately hired away by a competitor, and has hopefully gone on to engineering greatness.

What did we learn? To question — always question — conventional wisdom, and to explore every aspect of a project, whether it is in our area of expertise or not. Ask the "dumb questions" such as "Why can't this work?" Sometimes the simplest question (such as "Why can't we do something?") can lead to amazing breakthroughs.

My advice to you is:
- Integrate, integrate, integrate.
- Work with multiple models/interpretations.
- Learn how to communicate uncertainties to your peers and others.
- Realize that most things are not as simple as they appear.
- Seek experience and expertise, ask for advice, and share your ideas.
- Be persistent!

Postscript

In putting together this book, those of us on the committee realized that anyone who has been in this industry for more than 10 years has stories or advice worth sharing. In our many committee meetings, we shared some of our own stories, and in doing so, realized that they should be included as well.

So what follows are our summaries. They are included not because we see ourselves as legends, not even in our own minds, but because our stories do contribute to our heritage — as do your stories. It is our hope that someday you will have the opportunity to share your stories with someone, so that you too may add your own piece to the rich tapestry that is the heritage of the petroleum geologist.

Robert C. Shoup

Career history

1955	Born in Winona, Minnesota
1978	B.A. degree in geology, Winona State University
1980	M.S. degree in geology, University of Oklahoma
1980–1994	Shell Oil Company, New Orleans and Houston
1994–1995	Shell China Petroleum Company, Beijing
1996–1999	Shell Deepwater Inc., New Orleans
1999–2002	Samson Offshore Company, Houston
2002–present	Hilcorp Energy Company, Houston

My proudest accomplishments

One of my proudest accomplishments to date involves drilling a discovery on a prospect that some individuals had previously condemned. The prospect consisted of a large structural nose trapped against a salt mass. There was amplitude support; however, the amplitude abruptly terminated along the strike of the structure. Where the amplitude was observed, it had a reasonably good fit to structure. Because of the observation that the amplitude did not extend across the whole structural nose, several previous workers had condemned the prospect.

The horizon tied to a reservoir that was the major pay in several fields around the same salt-withdrawal minibasin, and I was sure that I was seeing pay here as well. To convince management to drill the well, however, I had to explain why the amplitude terminated as it did.

I mapped the event in detail, picking every trace and line. I mapped the loops above and below the event, and with regional isopach maps, I reconstructed the evolution of the minibasin. I demonstrated that as the reservoir was being deposited, two separate salt wings merged at the prospect. As the salt bodies sutured, there was a significant steepening of the dip along that flank, triggering a mass wasting event that erosively removed the reservoir from the west flank of the structure. Because of the detailed mapping, you could even see several scallop-shaped regions along the margin of the slide, where slope failure had occurred.

After I explained why the amplitude had terminated, management approved the well. On Christmas Eve 1997, the log came in with more than 90 feet of pay. That was one of the neatest Christmas presents I've ever had.

My biggest disappointment

My biggest disappointment was in having to return early from our assignment in China. We were very fortunate to have had the opportunity to live in China. When we learned that we were going, we decided as a family that we wanted to use this opportunity to learn about another people and culture. So when we arrived, we sought and made many Chinese friends.

My biggest challenge there was to learn how to work effectively with the team from China National Offshore Company that was assigned to work in our office. They had very different work habits and priorities than we did. Nevertheless, by working with them and learning and respecting their culture and opinions, we established a very strong and friendly working relationship.

We had been in China for almost two years, during a very dynamic period of change in that country. We had a great time and learned a great deal. So when Pecten, U.S. Shell's international subsidiary, decided to cut back its program in China and recall us to the States, all of us were deeply disappointed.

Anecdotal story

My most memorable well-sitting experience was on a prospect called Rodan. This was a great prospect, a sure thing. The prospect was characterized by a strong seismic amplitude with a very pronounced fit to structure. Seismic sequence analysis indicated a correlation with sand-prone facies, and gas chimneys were observed along adjacent faults. We solicited several partners, all of whom considered this prospect to be a "slam dunk."

Most logging runs seem to occur on weekends and in the wee hours of the morning, and this well was no exception. So it was that at 2:00 o'clock on a Sunday morning, I was sitting in the "company man's" office watching the LWD. As the gamma-ray tool crossed the objective, it dutifully kicked to the left. The resistivity tool lagged behind the gamma ray by 10 minutes, so I still didn't know if we had pay. Finally, after a very long 10 minutes, the resistivity shot to the right. Eureka, we had pay! The gamma ray was still showing nice clean sand, so this was promising to be a big well.

I started to do a quick reserve estimate in my head, when suddenly the resistivity shot back to the baseline. This couldn't be — the gamma ray was still in sand. Maybe there was a small shale break the gamma ray had missed. But no, the resistivity never went back up. We had found 9 feet of pay on water. In 4000 feet of water, that was the same as a dry hole.

All too often, the well that is a sure thing or declared to be a "slam dunk" ends up being a cement storage facility. There is always uncertainty.

My advice

Be active in your local geological society and/or AAPG. Serve on committees, run for office, and become certified. You will find that through this service, not only will you grow professionally, you will also make a great number of professional contacts. This network will prove invaluable during your career. If you ever want or need to change companies or to know who is buying good prospects or selling one, this network will be your single best resource.

Acknowledgments

As I mentioned in the introduction of this book, I am truly grateful to Blair Parrott. Not only did he help me find sharks' teeth, but with his guidance, I learned how to slip logs, how to properly use paleo, and how to predict reservoir. From Billy Frank, I learned how to correlate seismic and make maps, and from both of them, how to find and present good prospects. From Dr. John Donovan at Winona State and from Dr. John Wickham at OU, I developed and nurtured my long-lasting love affair for geology, an affair that continues to this day.

I am grateful to my father, Robert Shoup, from whom I learned the true value of professionalism and the realization that what you get out of life is proportional to what you put in. Within the AAPG family, I thank Don O'Nesky for the same reasons, and Norma Newby, Donna Riggs, Vickie Beighle, Michelle Mayfield, Randa Reeder-Briggs, and Diane Keim for all the help they have given me over the years.

In addition to those I have mentioned, I have been inspired by people whom I have been privileged to have known through the years. Although the list is longer than I can include here, some of the most notable are Chuck Roripaugh, Jim Hartman, Rufus LeBlanc, John Karlo, Doug Beckman, John Amoruso, Jim Lewis, Pete Rose, Jim Gibbs, Bruno Hanson, Bob Cowdery, Toby Carleton, Deborah Sacrey, Charles Sternbach, and Michel Halbouty.

Finally, I am grateful to my wife and children, whose love keep me going and whose spending habits keep me working.

Deborah K. Sacrey

Career history

1953	Born in Oklahoma City, Oklahoma
1976	B.S. in geology, University of Oklahoma
1976–1978	Gulf Oil Company, Midcontinent District, Oklahoma City
1978–1981	Michigan Wisconsin Pipe Line Company, Oklahoma City
1981–1986	Consultant, Oklahoma City
1986–1989	Chief geologist, Peko Oil/Week Exploration, Dallas/Houston
1990–1991	Consultant, Paramount Petroleum
1992–present	Consultant/independent, Auburn Energy

Proudest accomplishments

I have many proud accomplishments, one of which is having been responsible for finding $100MM value of gas in the Queen City play in south Texas. I am also proud to be involved in various activities in the AAPG, where I have met some of my dearest friends and most respected mentors.

Biggest disappointment

My biggest disappointment is a really expensive 15,000-foot dry hole I caused to be drilled on top of Wilburton Mountain in southeastern Oklahoma. I was a junior geologist with about five years of experience in the Arkoma Basin, and I just knew this was going to be a huge discovery in the Spiro Sand. The old adage of "never fall in love with your own prospects" proved to be true!

An anecdotal story

While working as a consultant for Paramount Petroleum, I developed expertise at drafting and "packaging" prospects in the Gulf Coast. After Nuevo purchased Paramount, I was released from my consulting agreement. With little Gulf Coast experience and with virtually no jobs to be had, I used these skills to open a drafting company. Within four years, I had six employees and was "packaging" deals for many independents in Houston.

It was the connections made from the drafting company that led to much of my 3-D consulting when I put my workstation together in 1996, and I have been busy with interpretation work since then. Now I am in a position where I have partners to purchase leases/seismic, and I take working interest in wells we drill.

My advice to you is:

Network, network, network! The time and effort I have put into various organizations not only garnered me wonderful friends and mentors, but the "public" exposure and willingness to work brought fiscal opportunities as well. In addition, make use of the skill sets you have, regardless of how "low" you think they are. You never know when your toe in the door at one level will lead to greater opportunities at another level.

Charles A. Sternbach

Career history
Born 1957

1980	B.A. degree in geology, Columbia University
1981–1984	M.S. and Ph.D. in geology, Rensselaer Polytechnic Institute
1984–1997	Staff geologist, Shell, Houston
1997–present	Jordan Oil and Gas, Houston

My proudest accomplishments to date include the following:

I am involved in some exciting exploration programs whose outcomes are pending. In the meantime, I would have to say my proudest accomplishments include being the exploration geologist for five new gas field discoveries (reserves exceeded 100 BCF) as a new hire at Shell during rejuvenation of the Michigan Basin in the mid-1980s, when subtle deep structures produced gas from Prairie du Chien sandstones. This was a great taste of success for a young geologist.

It was a thrill to have been able to evaluate exploration potential of 35 producing properties in the Permian Basin through the eyes of an explorationist at a time when 3-D seismic was new. It also helped to rescale the engineer's maps from 1:500' to a grander 1:8000' (or larger). New reserves were found, and a significant corporate effort ensued.

My desire to assemble trend plays has led me to create and pursue significant opportunities in the Lodgepole, Cotton Valley, and other onshore reef plays where I have played important roles in raising capital exceeding $25 MM. I am drawn to reefs by my education and because they are rich targets suitable to projection along trend using carbonate geologic insights.

I am proud of having capitalized on educational opportunities, from public education at Stuyvesant High School in New York City to completing both my M.S. and Ph.D. in three-and-a-half years at Rensselaer with a 4.0 GPA. I have also been proud to serve in professional societies: HGS president at 41, Legends programs (2000, 2003), co-general vice chair AAPG 2002 (Technical Program), and Discoverers of the 20th Century (with Marlan Downey). The Legends and Discoverers programs and this Heritage publication mean a lot to me because we should honor our forebears.

My biggest disappointment

My biggest disappointment was searching for another Wilburton field (400 BCF) in the Arkoma Basin and not finding one. By careful study of the trap components of Wilburton, it became clear to me that more than 100 dry holes in the basin, including dozens of industry dry holes drilled after Wilburton, lacked the critical fault-seal requirements that Wilburton possessed. Although finding hydrocarbons is always more fun than not, by realizing this critical insight early, we added only one "data point" to regional control where we could have added many. And maybe someday this work will help us find a future opportunity.

Anecdotal story

"**Something hidden, go and find it!**" Back in my early Michigan days, I met and became good friends with an old scout named Jim. Among Jim's many assets were a handshake so firm he could bring you to your knees, and the fact that he had been around long enough to know the early history of the basin. On one of his visits to my office, he told me "Find the old stratigraphic tests," and left. When my fingers recovered enough to dial, I set off a series of phone calls and made subsequent visits to files. After prolonged frustration that can come from trying to find things long hidden in company files — Eureka!

These records enabled use of a classical technique. By contouring a shallow marker bed from stratigraphic tests, I found a structural flexure that identified a deeper and subsequently productive gas field. Other such discoveries followed. Lessons learned: (1) Listen to the old guys, and (2) things such as stratigraphic tests may be "low tech," but use whatever works.

The independent life. I've always admired resourceful and determined independents, like many whose stores are included in this book, who started with nothing and wound up with something. So when I was among a fortunate few who piled into a Lear jet to review a reef play with legendary explorer Tom Jordan at his northern California office, I took notice. One morning, long after we had met, I was a guest at his winery. I was considering various career options and was in a reflective mood. As the sun rose over vineyards and singing birds, I said to myself, "Goodbye (name of former company), hello Jordan Oil and Gas!" I had resolved to join the independent ranks. Six years later, it is still a great honor to work with Tom Jordan, Dick Vincelette, Gary Griffith, and Bruce McClellan on the Jordan team.

Compound interest of lifelong friendships. I have found that friendships long maintained bring great pleasure and can enhance your life, often when you least expect it. One happy story occurred a few years ago when my Ph.D. professor Gerry Friedman called. He had introduced me to my wife, a fellow geology student, and had attended our wedding, now close to 20 years ago. I think it meant as much to me to be able to thank him by writing his Sidney Powers citation as it did to him for him to receive the award!

My advice:

My advice is to be aware of opportunities created by changing conditions. Good exploration stories, especially those in mature areas, have "a twist." Something obvious now might not have been seeable, sought, or available earlier. Restrictions resulting from politics, technology or mind-set often change. Old seismic data and well records can be valuable when processed with new software or fresh ideas. And because we often get what we look for, we might as well be bold and think big!

Maintain "outward focus." By regularly attending HGS and AAPG meetings (I estimate about 300 talks during 15 years), I have been privileged to hear about new plays, discoveries, and exploration techniques by those who made them happen. Make a habit of attending society meetings, taking courses, and shaking new hands.

Cultivate a good memory by active learning and staying curious in many subjects. It seems to me that (1) the more I learn, the more I want to learn, and (2) memory improves with use. Creating good files and folios can help. Read extensively, including Levorsen, Pratt, Degolyer, and especially everything Michel T. Halbouty has ever written!

Seek and keep good friendships. They are the greatest gifts in life.

Richard L. Nagy

Career history
Born September 7, 1952

1976	B.S. degree in geology, San Diego State University
1977–1978	Mud logger for Borst & Giddons Well Logging Co.
1978–1980	Graduate geology studies, San Diego State University
1980–1982	Development geologist for Phillips Petroleum Company
1982–1989	Exploration geologist for American Petrofina Co.
1989	Consulting geologist
1990–2002	Exploration Geologist for Phillips Petroleum Company
2002–present	Exploration geologist for ConocoPhillips

My proudest accomplishments

I consider my proudest accomplishment to be a very encompassing continuity of focus and determination that has aided me in being successful professionally. Not only in the technical side of performing a geologic evaluation or study or drilling for oil and gas, but over the years, I have been rewarded by many friends, colleagues, and associates throughout the oil business. They have given me many great experiences that have helped me to grow as a person and a professional. A good example of this was being asked to join with the other editors of this publication to help in bringing about documentation of the wisdom of some of our profession's legends.

On a personal note, I also consider my wife, Debbie, and three children, Erin, Jeff, and Erica, and their growth as something I am very proud of.

My biggest disappointment

I have always somewhat regretted not finishing graduate school and attaining a master's degree in geology, but it was a decision I made at the time.

I can't think of a single big disappointment in my professional career, as far as drilling goes. Of course there were many "learnings" that I've experienced and then said, "Boy, I'll never do that again." There were times when I wished I could have convinced my management to follow up on my recommendations, but I've always had the attitude to live and learn and move on.

Anecdotal story

One of the themes of this publication is the role and value of a mentor in our lives and profession. I can remember my first night as a mud logger — my first job out of school. I was working with a real old-timer. Even though I had looked at plenty of rocks as a student, it was really quite different on the rig, working very quickly to catch samples, clean them, and then do a sample description. By then, it was time to catch the next sample.

At first, it seemed I got everything wrong, from cleaning the sample to describing it, but with the guidance of Stan, I quickly learned, and the job got easier. This same process essentially repeated itself several years later, when Phillips hired me as a development geologist. One of the more senior geologists on the staff used to get into the office pretty early, as I did. He shared many experiences and how-to knowledge with me. During one early morning discussion, I discovered that he knew Stan from my stint as mud logger many years before, and we had a good time with that.

My advice

My advice for all those just entering the business is to never give up on your ideas. Be persistent but be patient. Develop an optimistic attitude, and never stop seeking new knowledge (even if it is from old files). Try to find someone who can provide some mentoring support. Membership in local and national geological societies can also help in developing a network. The AAPG and Houston Geological Society have helped me tremendously in keeping up with the latest technology and exploration concepts, as well as developing a network of mentors and friends to share ideas with.